AUTHENTIC TRANSCRIPTIONS WITH NOTES AND TABLATURE

Music transcriptions by Steve Gorenberg

Published by Wise Publications
8/9 Frith Street, London W1D 3JB, England.

Exclusive Distributors:
Music Sales Limited
Distribution Centre, Newmarket Road, Bury St. Edmunds, Suffolk IP33 3YB, England.
Music Sales Pty Limited
120 Rothschild Avenue, Rosebury, NSW 2018, Australia.

Order No. AM981013
ISBN 1-84449-730-5
This book © Copyright 2004 by Wise Publications.

Printed in the USA.

www.musicsales.com

Wise Publications
part of The Music Sales Group
London/New York/Paris/Sydney/Copenhagen/Berlin/Madrid/Tokyo

Last Chance

Words and Music by Chris Cester and Cameron Muncey

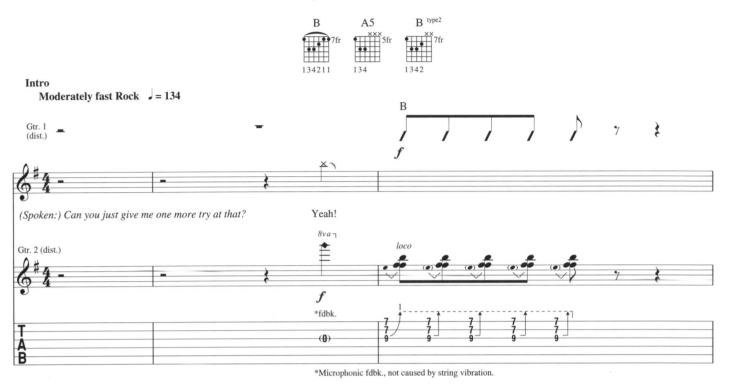

Intro

Moderately fast Rock ♩ = 134

(Spoken:) Can you just give me one more try at that?   Yeah!

*Microphonic fdbk., not caused by string vibration.

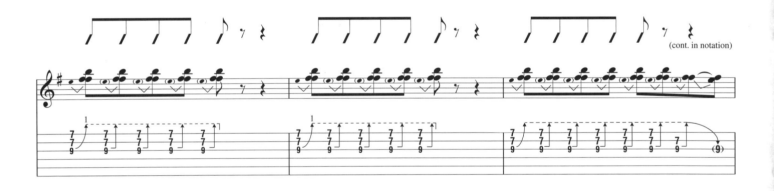

(cont. in notation)

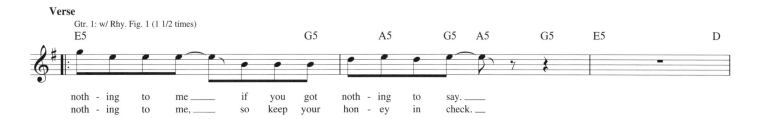

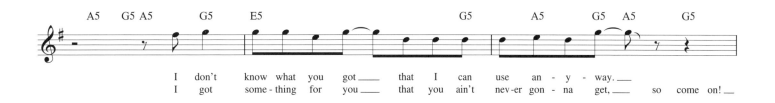

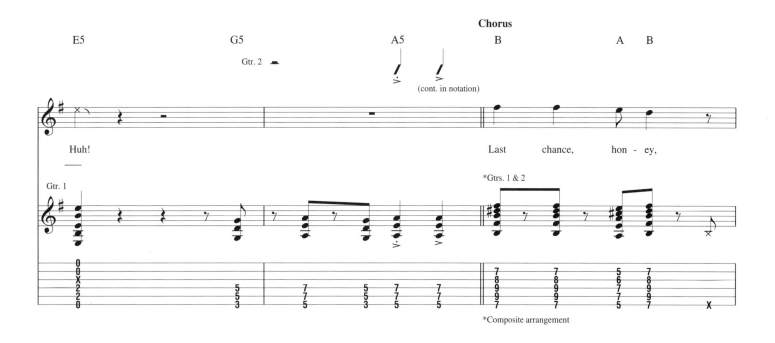

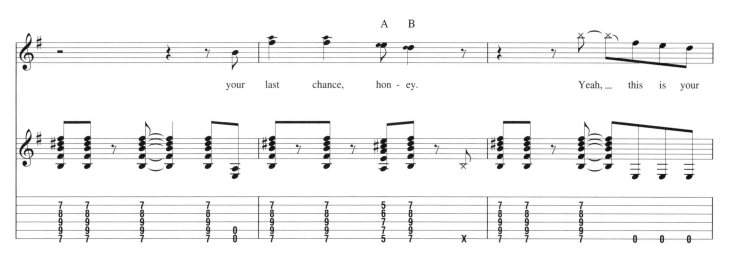

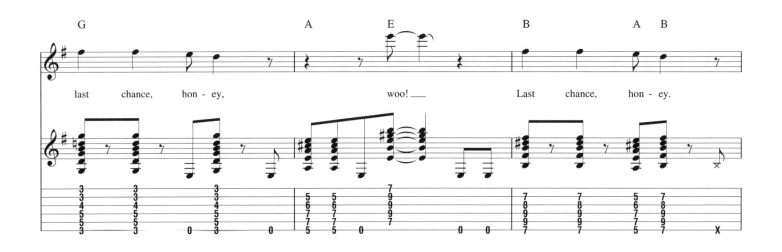

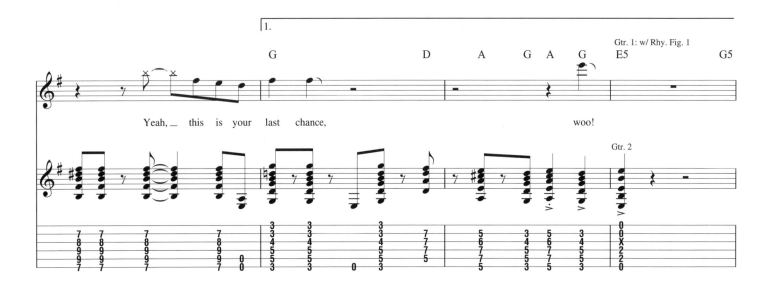

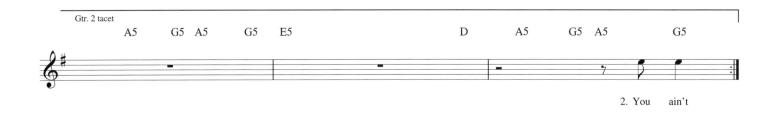

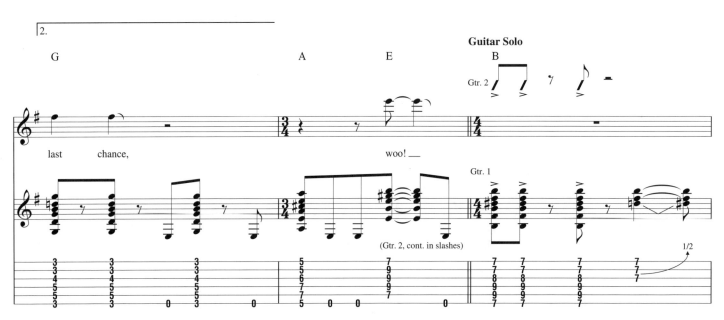

4

5

Are You Gonna Be My Girl

Words and Music by Nic Cester and Cameron Muncey

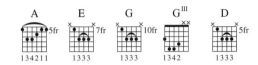

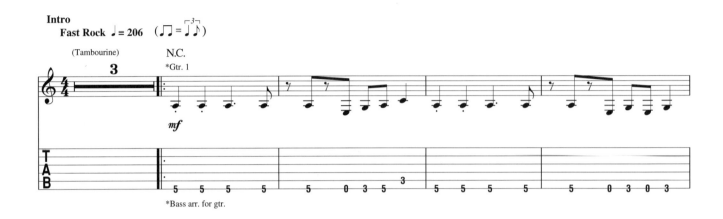

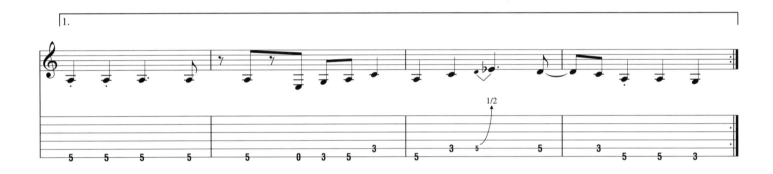

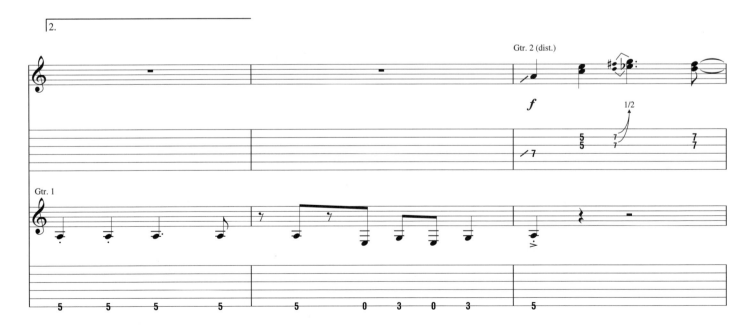

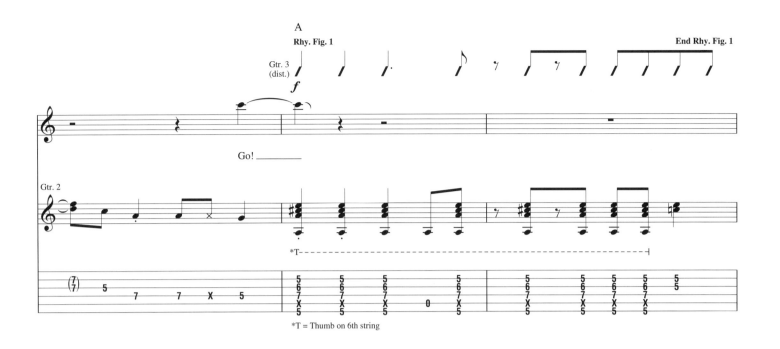

*T = Thumb on 6th string

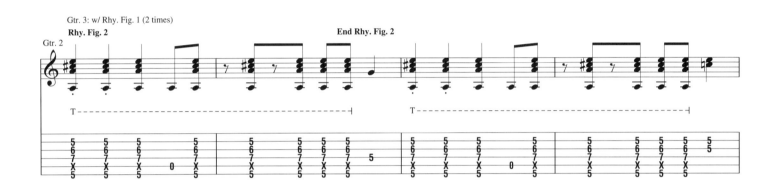

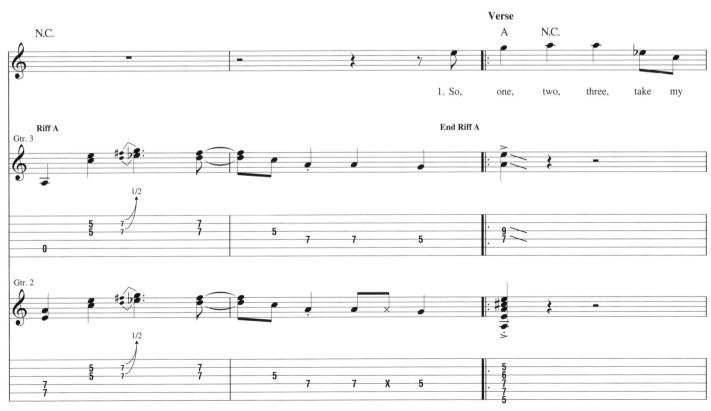

hand and come with me be- cause you look so fine and I real-ly want to make you mine.

I say you look so fine and I real-ly want to make you mine.

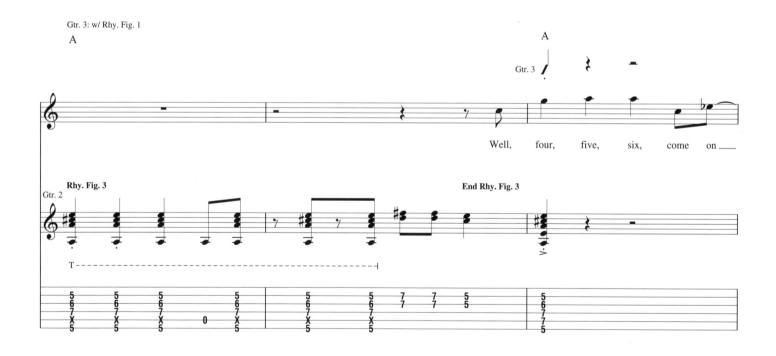

Well, four, five, six, come on ___

___ and get your kicks. Now you don't need mon- ey { when you look like that, do you, hon-ey? / with a face like that, do ya? }

Gtr. 3: w/ Rhy. Fig. 1

Gtr. 3: w/ Riff A

N.C.

Gtr. 2

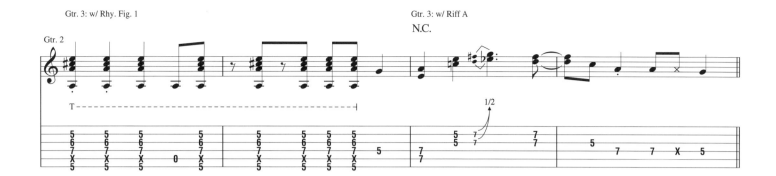

Pre-Chorus

Gtrs. 2 & 3: w/ Rhy. Fig. 4 (2 times)

D   C   G   D   C   G

Big ___ black ___ boots, ___   long ___ brown ___ hair. ___

Rhy. Fig. 4   **End Rhy. Fig. 4**

**Gtrs. 2 & 3

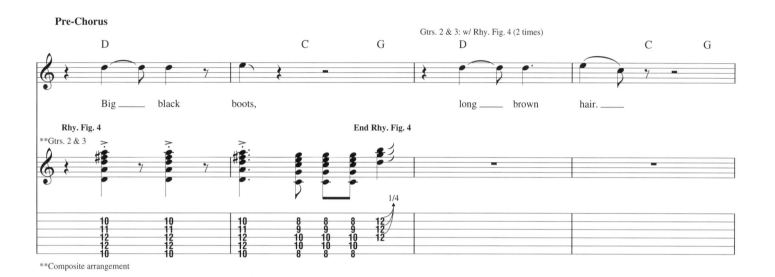

**Composite arrangement

D   C   G   D

She's ___ so sweet with ___ her   get ___ back ___ stare. ___

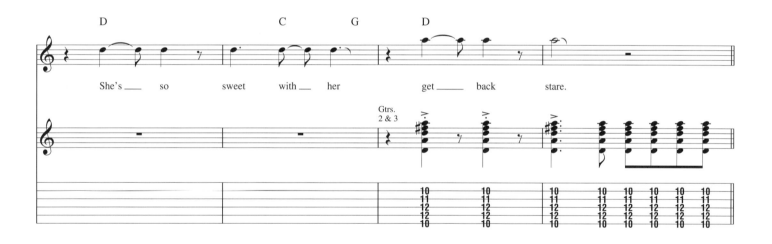

Chorus

A   C

Well, I could see ___   you home with me, ___

Rhy. Fig. 5

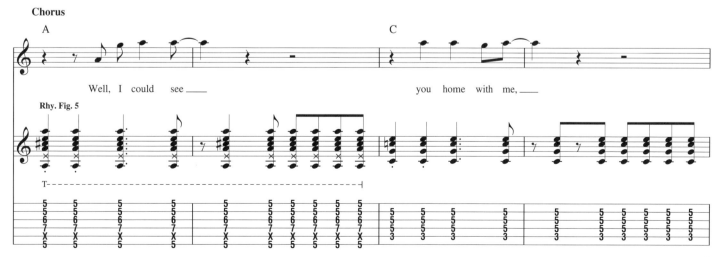

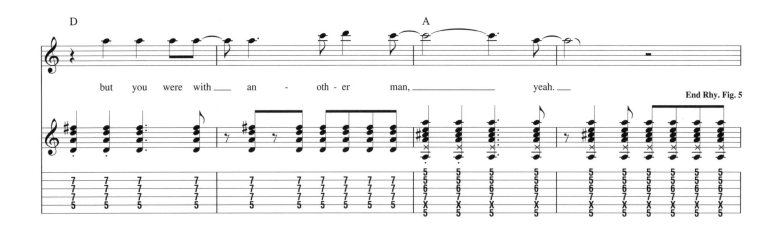

but you were with ___ an - oth - er man, _____ yeah. ___

End Rhy. Fig. 5

Gtrs. 2 & 3: w/ Rhy. Fig. 5

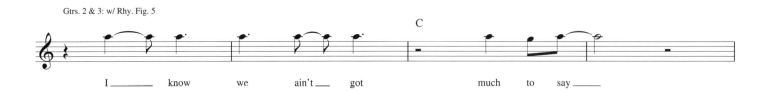

I _____ know we ain't ___ got much to say _____

be - fore I let _____ you get a - way, _____ yeah. ___

Gtr. 3

Gtr. 2

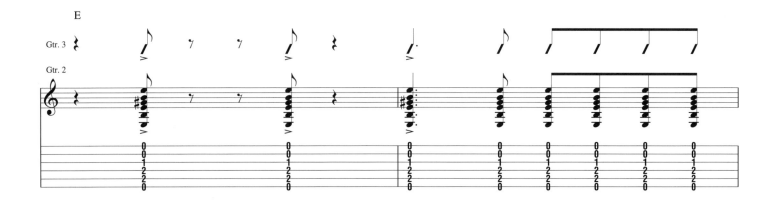

1.

I said, "Are you gon - na be my girl?" ___

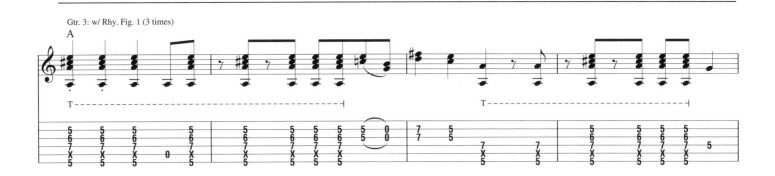

Gtr. 3: w/ Rhy. Fig. 1 (3 times)

A

Gtr. 3: w/ Riff A

N.C.

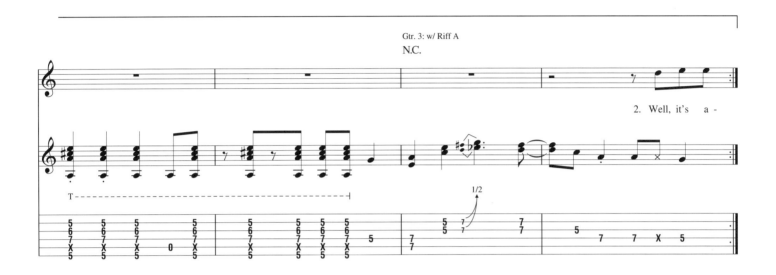

2. Well, it's a-

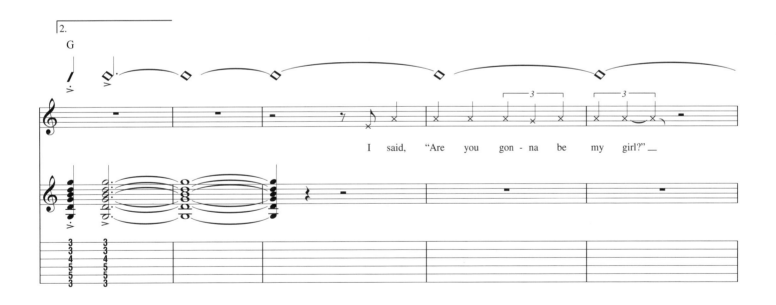

2.

G

I said, "Are you gon-na be my girl?" —

Gtr. 2: w/ Rhy. Fig. 2 (4 times)

Gtr. 3 tacet

A5

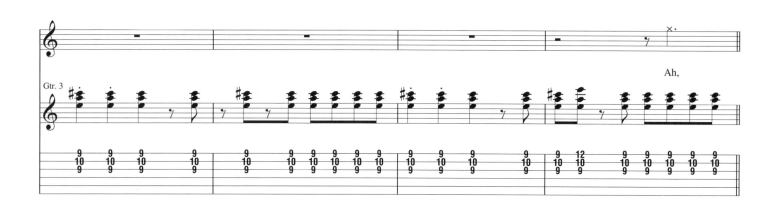

Guitar Solo

Gtr. 2: w/ Rhy. Fig. 2 (4 times)

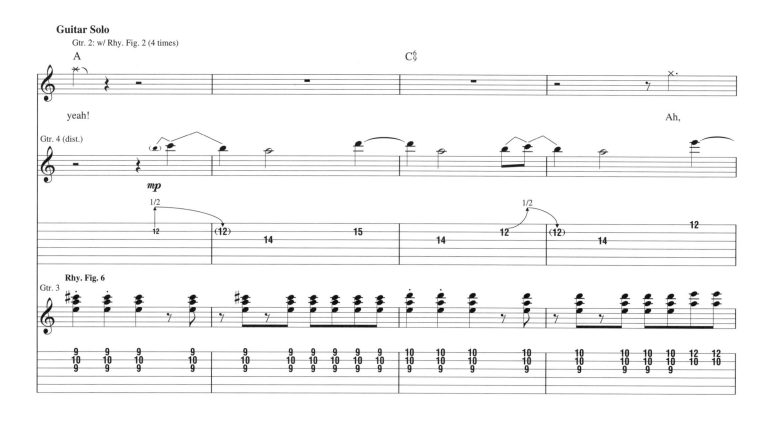

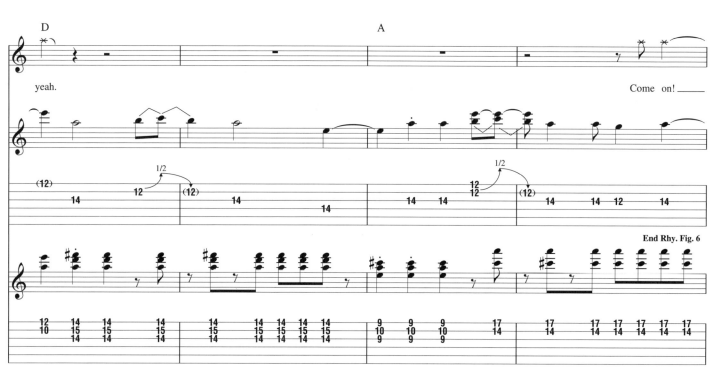

Gtr. 2: w/ Rhy. Fig. 3 (4 times)
Gtr. 3: w/ Rhy. Fig. 6

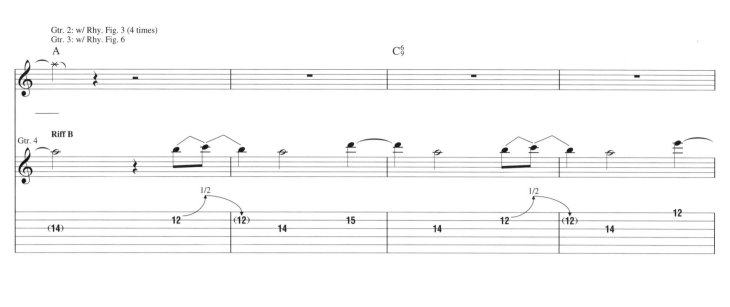

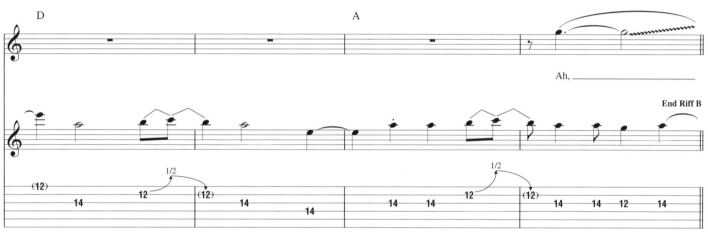

Ah, _____

Chorus

Gtrs. 2 & 3: w/ Rhy. Fig. 5 (2 times)
Gtr. 4: w/ Riff B (2 3/4 times)

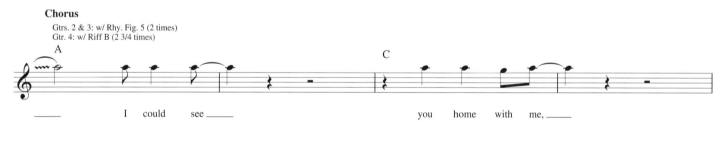

_____ I could see _____ you home with me, _____

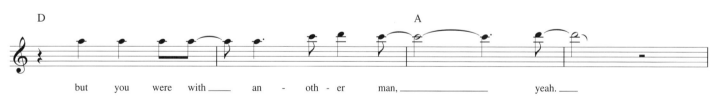

but you were with _____ an - oth - er man, _____ yeah. _____

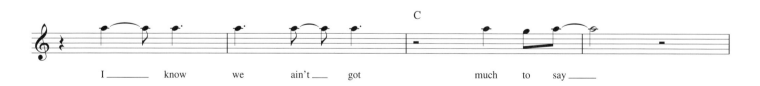

I _____ know we ain't _____ got much to say _____

be - fore I let _____ you get a - way, _____ yeah. _____

Gtr. 3: w/ Rhy. Fig. 5 (1st 6 meas.)
C
Uh, be my girl.
Be my
Gtr. 2
D
girl.
Are you gon - na be my
(cont. in slashes)
A
E G III E G III E
⑥ open ⑥ open ⑥ open
D
Gtrs. 2 & 3
girl?
Yeah!
Gtr. 4

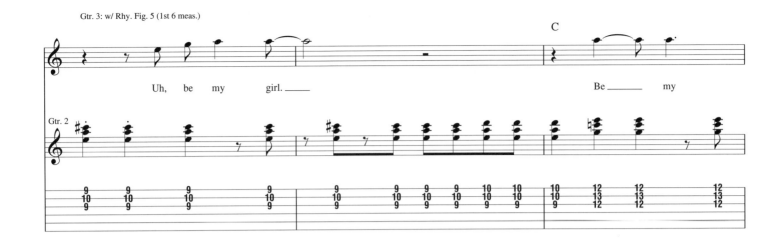

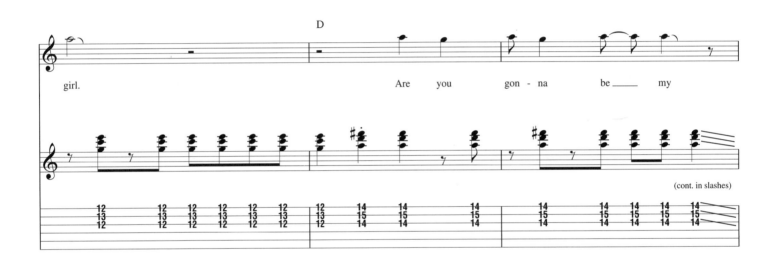

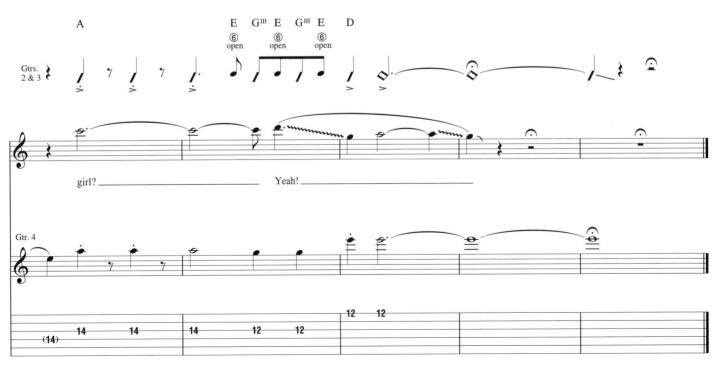

Rollover D.J.

Words and Music by Nic Cester and Cameron Muncey

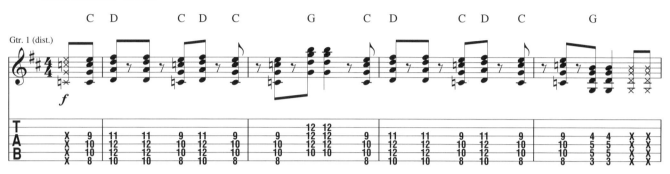

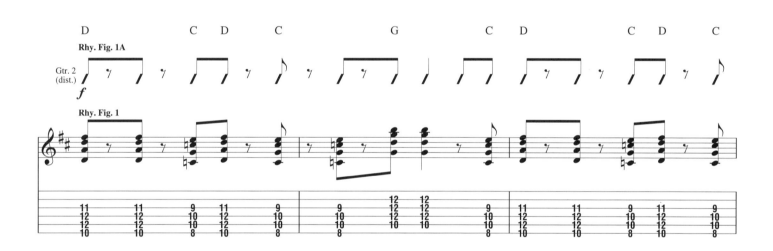

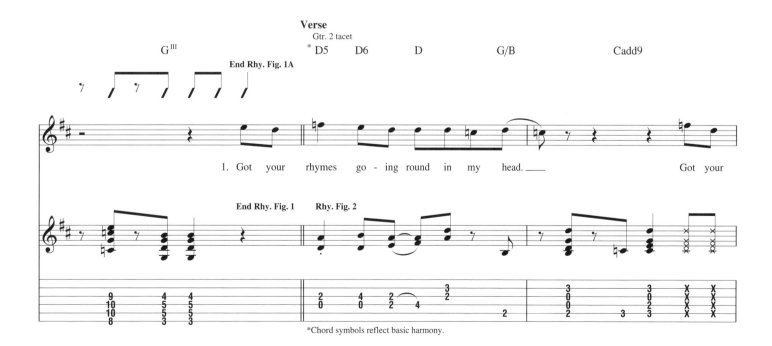

*Chord symbols reflect basic harmony.

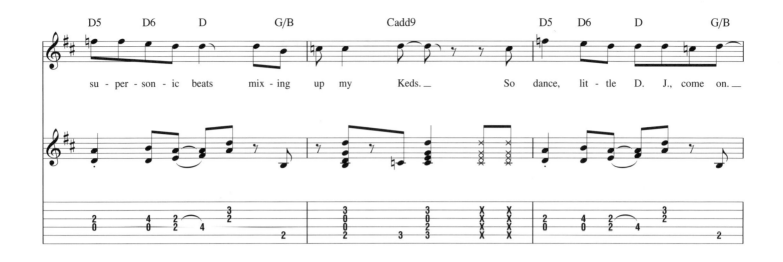

su-per-son-ic beats mix-ing up my Keds.___ So dance, lit-tle D. J., come on.___

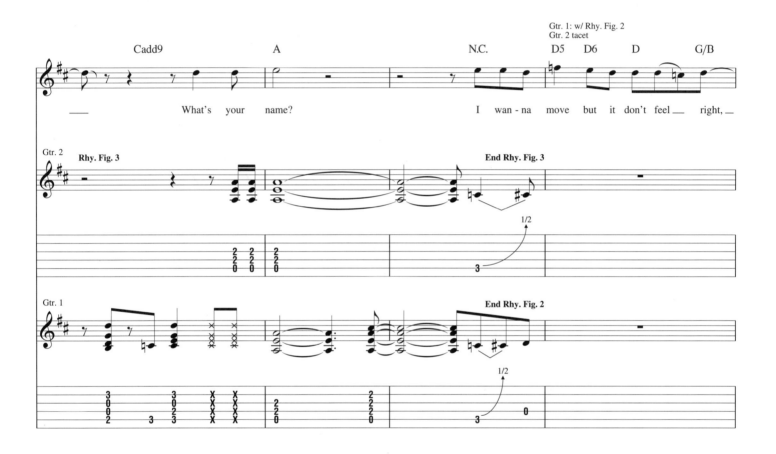

Gtr. 1: w/ Rhy. Fig. 2
Gtr. 2 tacet

___ What's your name? I wan-na move but it don't feel ___ right, ___

___ 'cause you've been play-ing oth-er peo-ple's songs ___ all night. ___ So

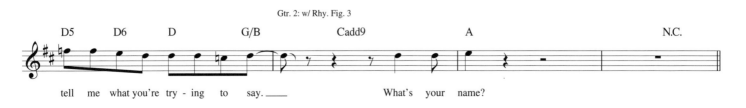

Gtr. 2: w/ Rhy. Fig. 3

tell me what you're try-ing to say. ___ What's your name?

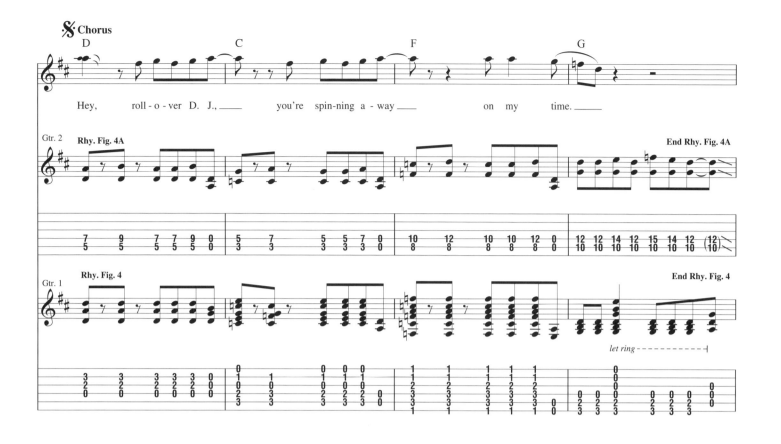

Hey, roll-o-ver D. J., _____ you're spin-ning a-way _____ on my time. _____

Hey, who cares what you play? _____ Say what-ev-er you say, _____ 'cause I don't mind. _____

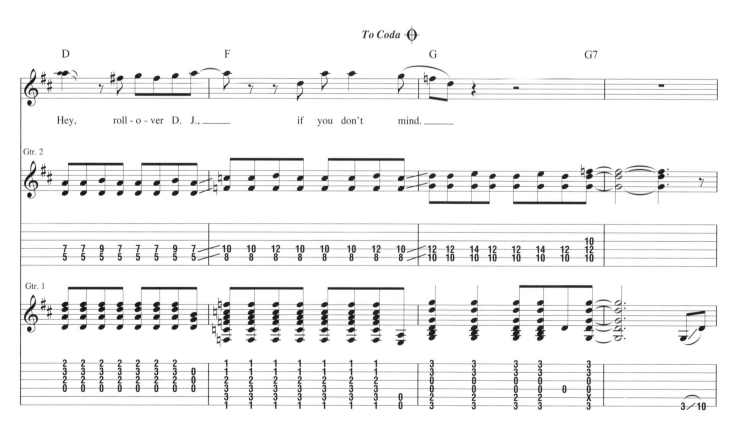

Hey, roll-o-ver D. J., _____ if you don't mind. _____

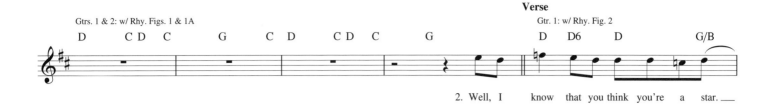

Gtrs. 1 & 2: w/ Rhy. Figs. 1 & 1A

Verse

Gtr. 1: w/ Rhy. Fig. 2

| D | C D C | G | C D | C D C | G | D D6 D | G/B |

2. Well, I know that you think you're a star. ___

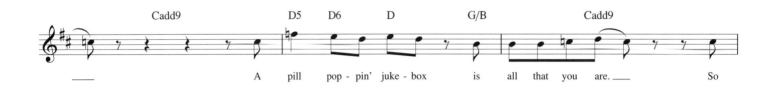

| Cadd9 | D5 D6 D | G/B | Cadd9 |

___ A pill pop - pin' juke - box is all that you are. ___ So

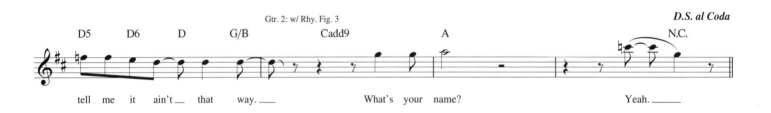

Gtr. 2: w/ Rhy. Fig. 3

D.S. al Coda

| D5 D6 D | G/B | Cadd9 | A | N.C. |

tell me it ain't ___ that way. ___ What's your name? Yeah. ___

Coda

G open

Gtr. 1

(cont. in notation)

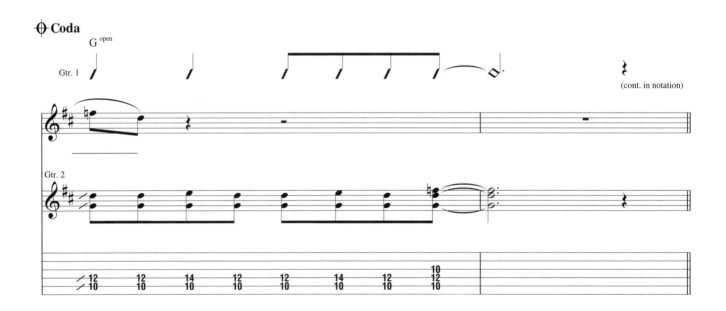

Gtr. 2

1.

Interlude

Gtr. 2 tacet

Gtr. 1

| D5 D6 | D5 D6 C5 | C6 C5 C6 | G5 G6 G5 G6 G5 | G6 G7 G6 |

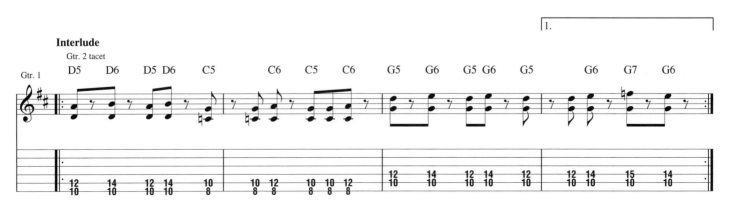

18

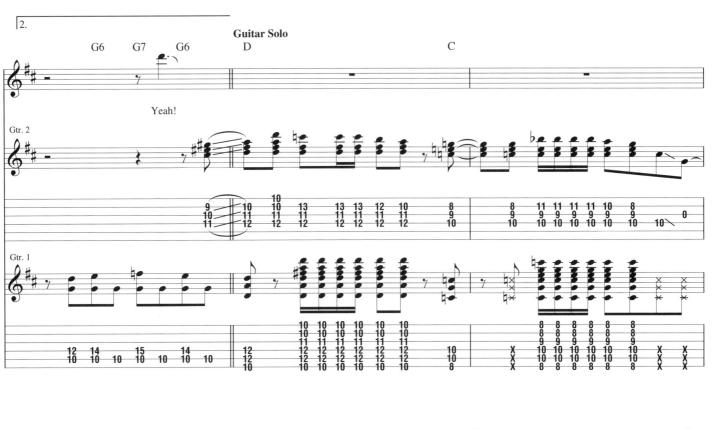

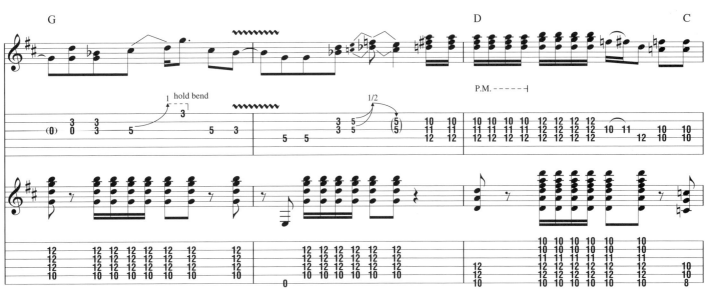

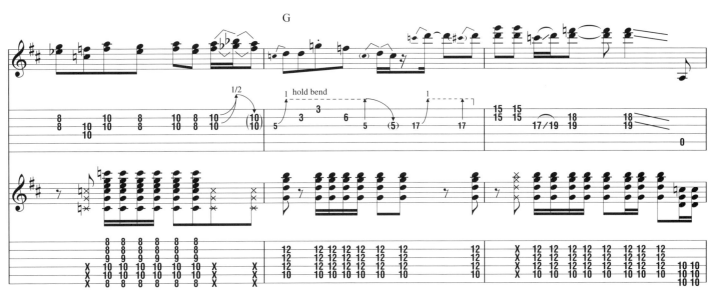

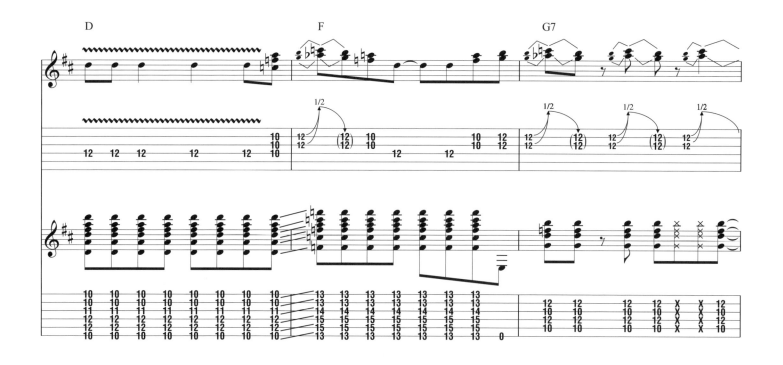

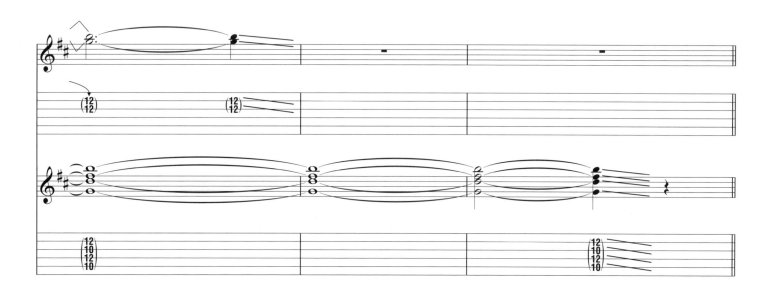

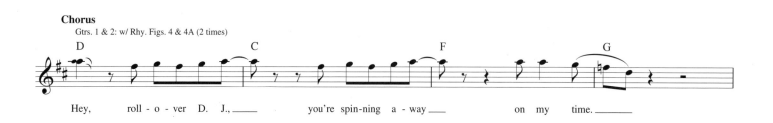

Chorus
Gtrs. 1 & 2: w/ Rhy. Figs. 4 & 4A (2 times)

Hey, roll-o-ver D. J.,___ you're spin-ning a-way___ on my time.___

Hey, who cares what you play?___ Say what-ev-er you say,___ 'cause I don't mind.

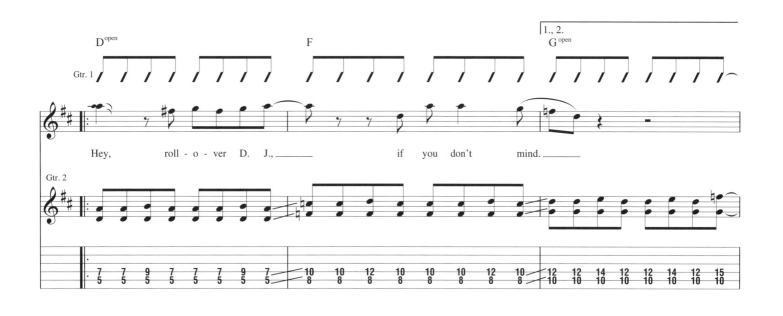

Hey, roll - o - ver D. J., _____ if you don't mind. _____

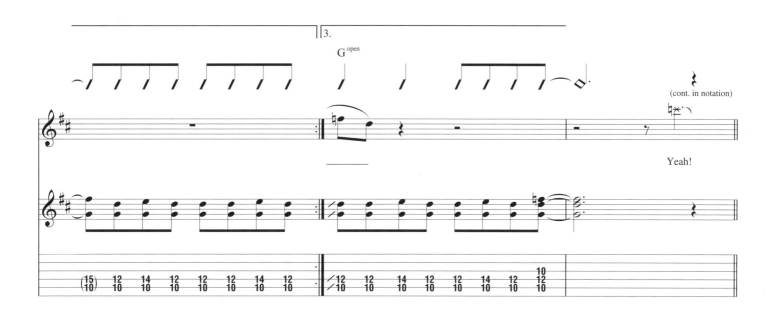

(cont. in notation)

Yeah!

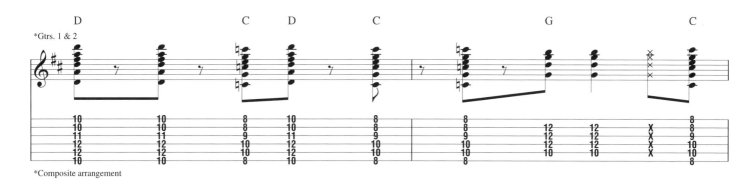

*Composite arrangement

Look What You've Done

Words and Music by Nic Cester

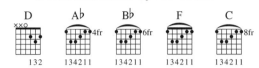

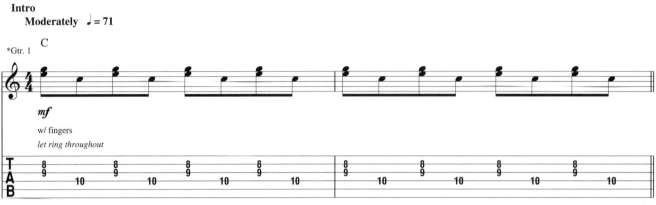

Intro
Moderately ♩ = 71

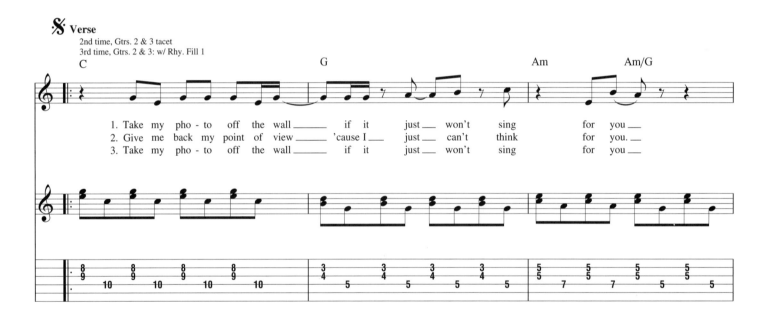

1. Take my pho-to off the wall ____ if it just ____ won't sing for you ____
2. Give me back my point of view ____ 'cause I ____ just ____ can't think for you. ____
3. Take my pho-to off the wall ____ if it just ____ won't sing for you ____

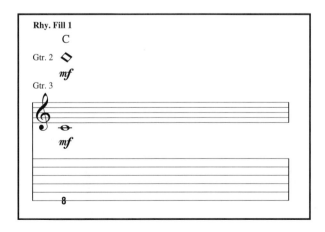

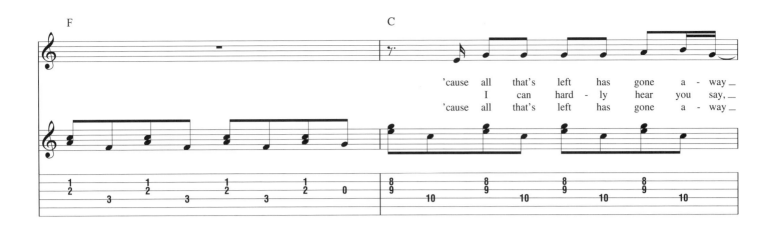

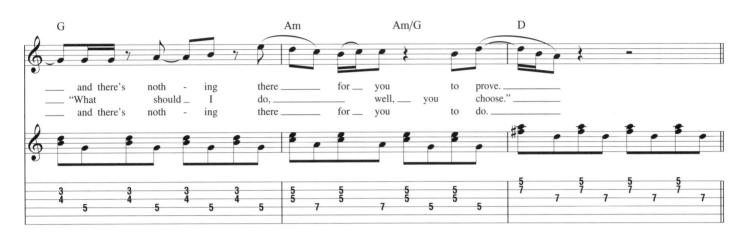

Chorus

Gtr. 1 tacet

3rd time, Gtr. 3: w/ Fill 1

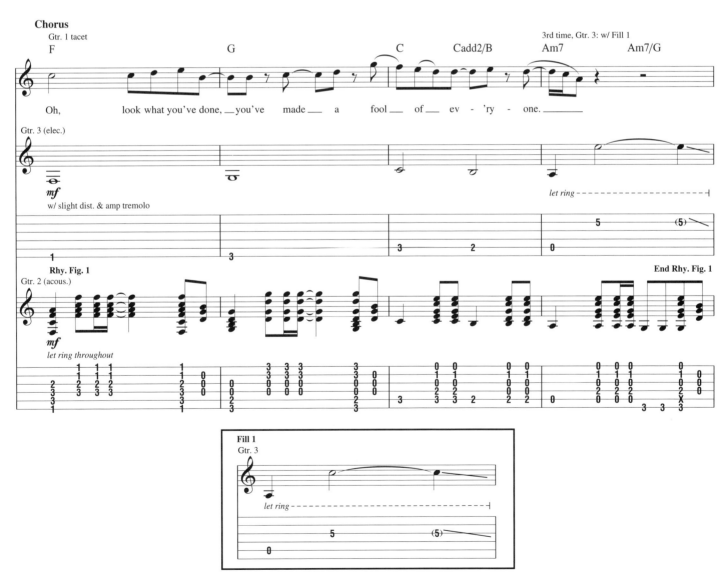

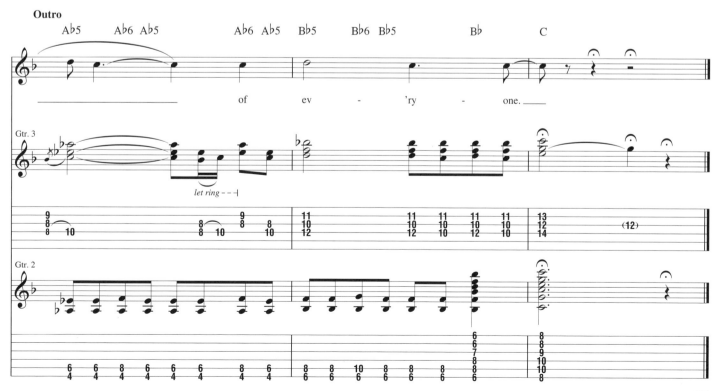

Get What You Need

Words and Music by Nic Cester, Chris Cester and Cameron Muncey

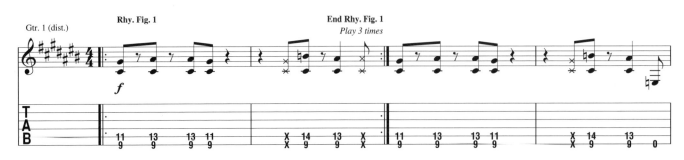

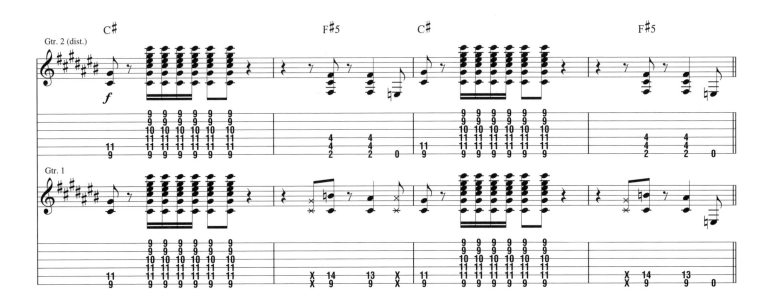

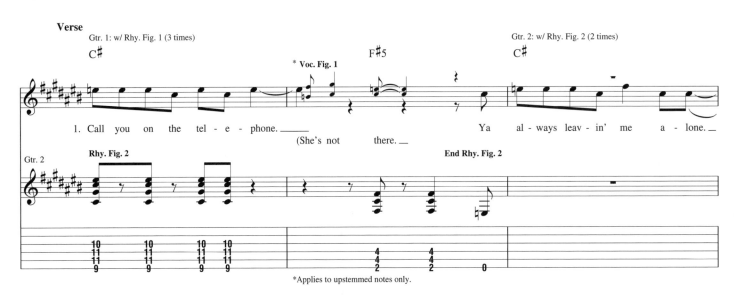

*Applies to upstemmed notes only.

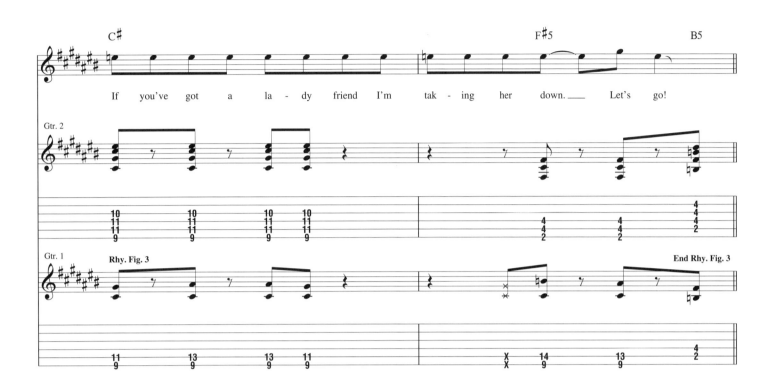

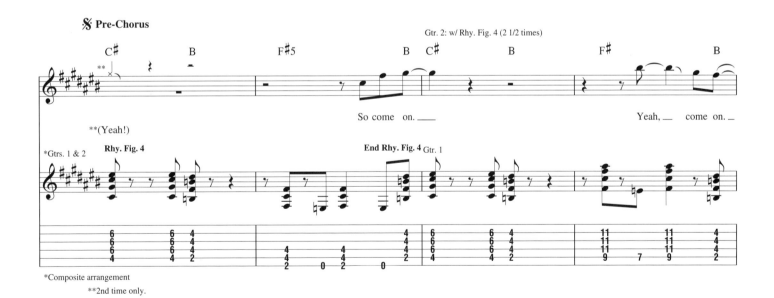

*Composite arrangement

**2nd time only.

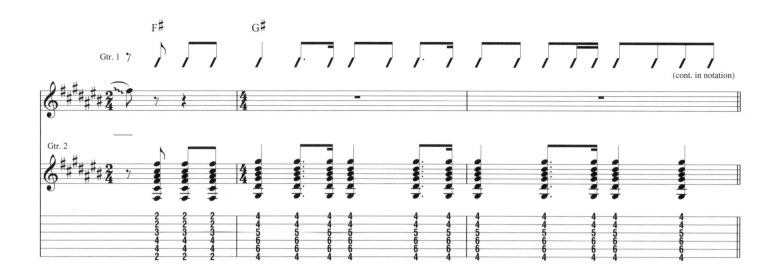

Interlude

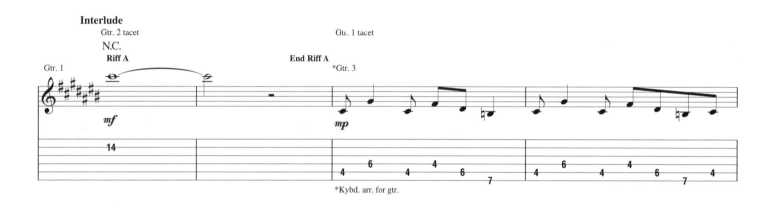

*Gradually lift P.M.

Chorus

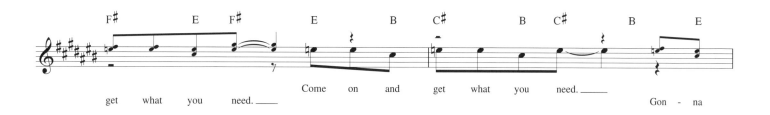

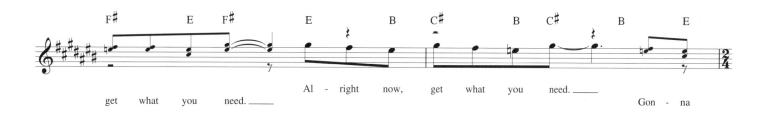

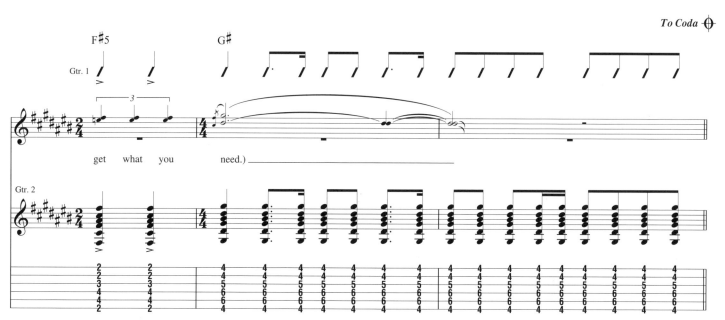

Interlude

Gtr. 1: w/ Riff A
Gtr. 2 tacet

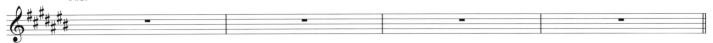

Verse

N.C.

2. Now I'm in a rock-in' band. _____ (She's not   there.) __   No one has to hold   my   hand. __

D.S. al Coda

Gtrs. 1 & 2: w/ Rhy. Figs. 1 & 2

C#   F#5   Gtr. 1: w/ Rhy. Fig. 3   F#5   B5
                                                 C#

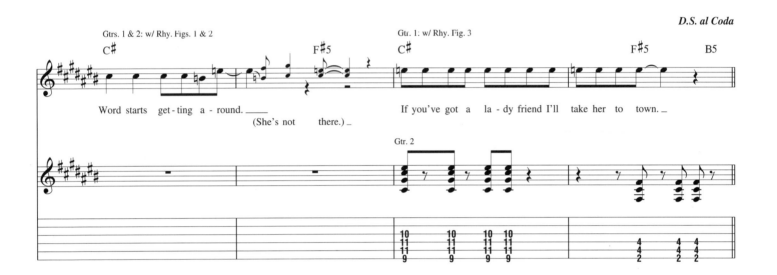

Word starts get-ting a-round. _____   If you've got a   la-dy friend I'll   take her to   town. __
(She's not   there.) __

Gtr. 2

Coda

Interlude

Gtr. 1: w/ Riff A
Gtr. 2 tacet

N.C.   C#5   C#6 C#5

Gtr. 4 (dist.)   Rhy. Fig. 6

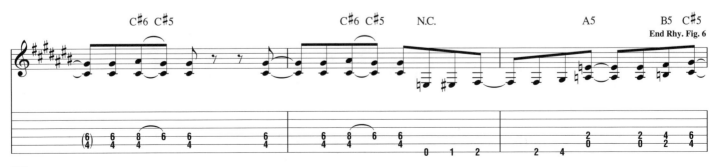

mf

C#6 C#5   C#6 C#5   N.C.   A5   B5 C#5
                                                                                   End Rhy. Fig. 6

Gtr. 4: w/ Rhy. Fig. 6

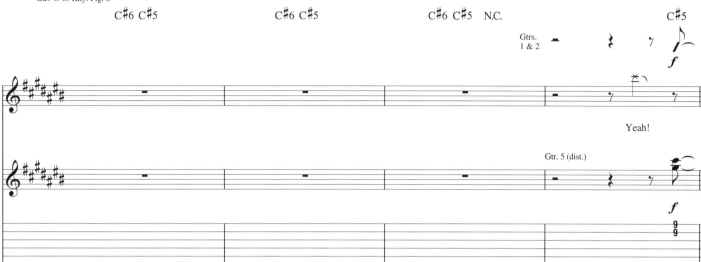

C#6 C#5   C#6 C#5   C#6 C#5   N.C.   C#5

Yeah!

Guitar Solo
Gtrs. 1, 2 & 4: w/ Rhy. Fig. 6 (4 times)

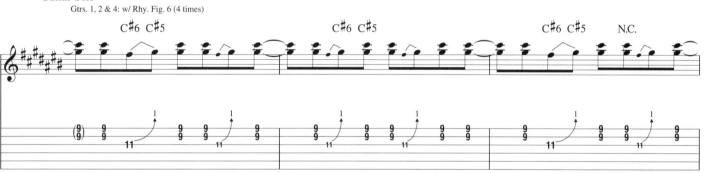

C#6 C#5   C#6 C#5   C#6 C#5   N.C.

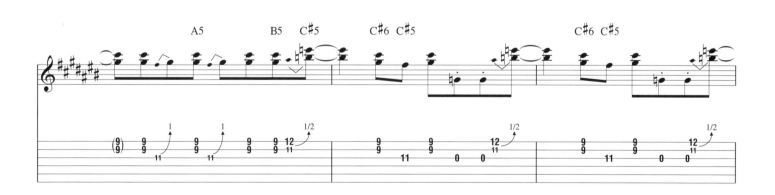

A5   B5   C#5   C#6 C#5   C#6 C#5

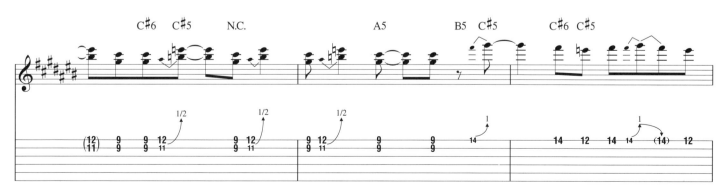

C#6   C#5   N.C.   A5   B5   C#5   C#6 C#5

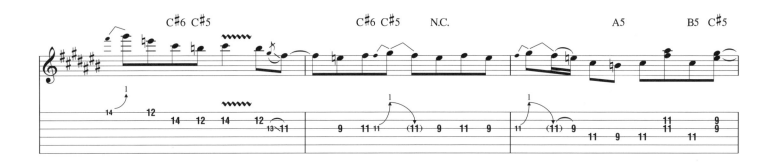

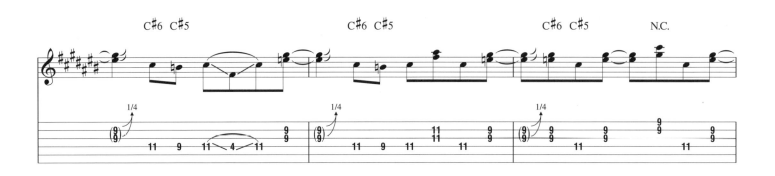

Chorus
Gtrs. 1 & 2: w/ Rhy. Figs. 5 & 5A (3 1/2 times)
Gtrs. 4 & 5 tacet

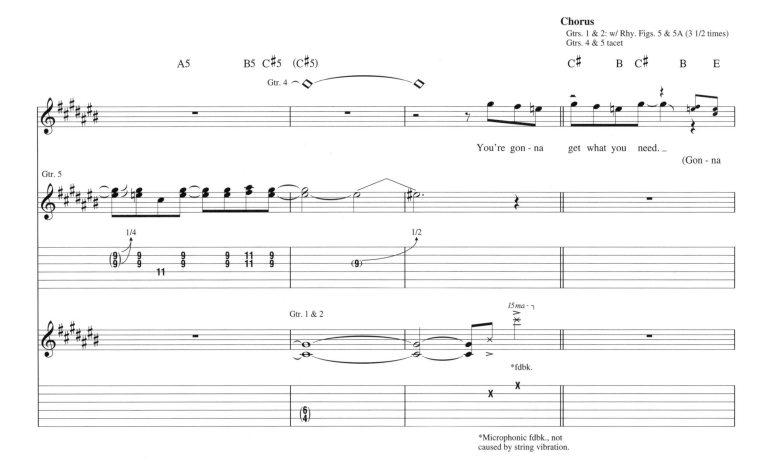

You're gon - na   get what you   need. __
(Gon - na

*Microphonic fdbk., not
caused by string vibration.

You're gon - na   get what you   need. __   Come on and
get what you   need. __   Gon - na   get what you   need. __

get what you need. ___
Gon - na   get what you need. ___   You're gon - na   get what you need. ___   Gon - na

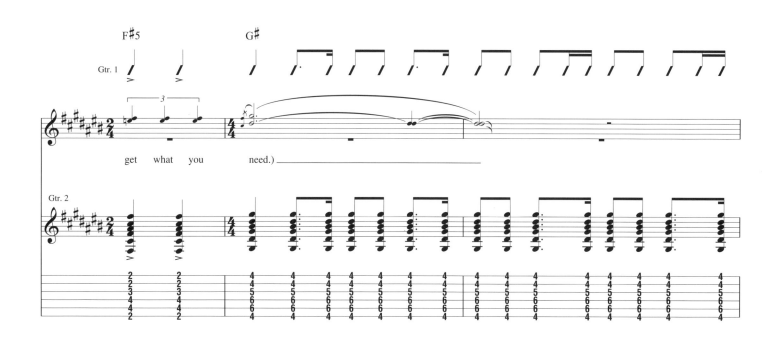

get   what   you   need.) ___

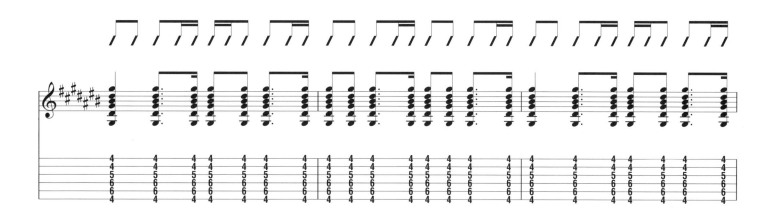

Free time

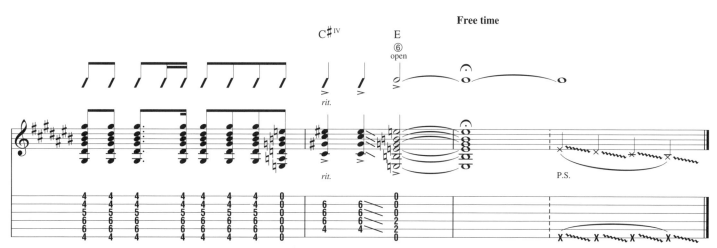

Move On

Words and Music by Nic Cester and Chris Cester

Gtr. 1: Capo III
Gtrs. 3, 4 & 5: Open G tuning:
(low to high) D-G-D-G-B-D

Intro
Free time

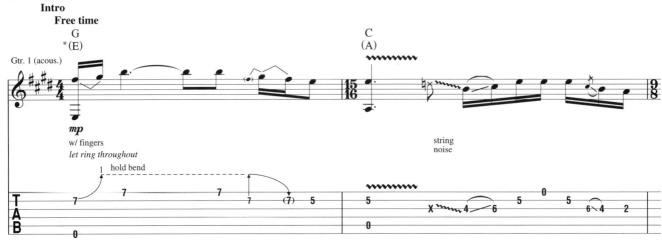

*Symbols in parentheses represent chord names respective to capoed guitar.
Symbols above reflect actual saounding chords (implied harmony). Capoed
fret is "0" in tab.

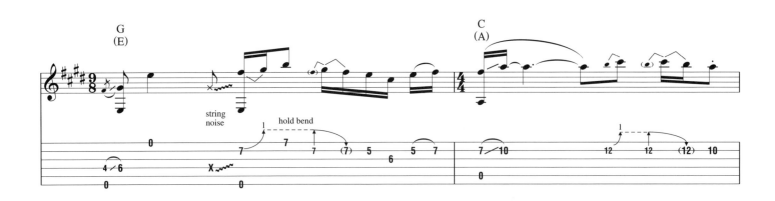

Slow ♩ = 60

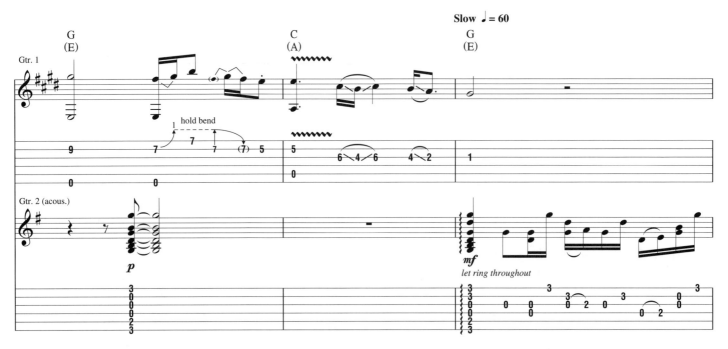

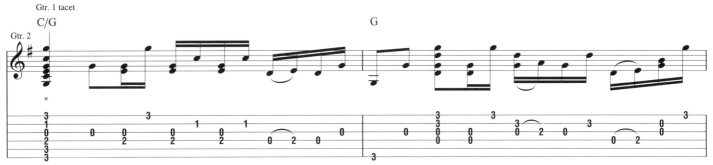

Gtr. 1 tacet

C/G

Gtr. 2

*Fret 5th & 6th strings w/ 3rd finger.

G

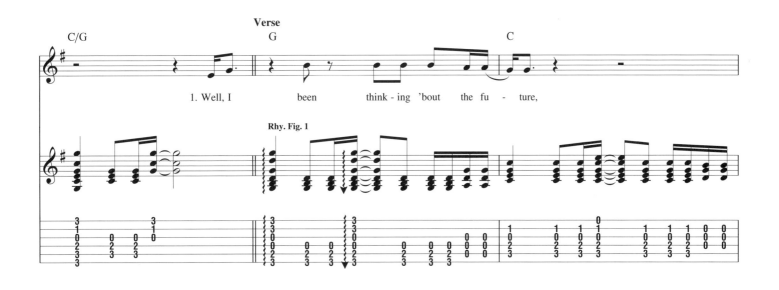

Verse

C/G   G   C

1. Well, I   been   think-ing 'bout the fu - ture,

Rhy. Fig. 1

G   C   G

but I'm too young to   pre-tend. ___   It's such   a waste   to al-ways look be-hind ___

C   G   C

___ you, ___   you should be look-in' straight a - head. ___

End Rhy. Fig. 1

35

Chorus

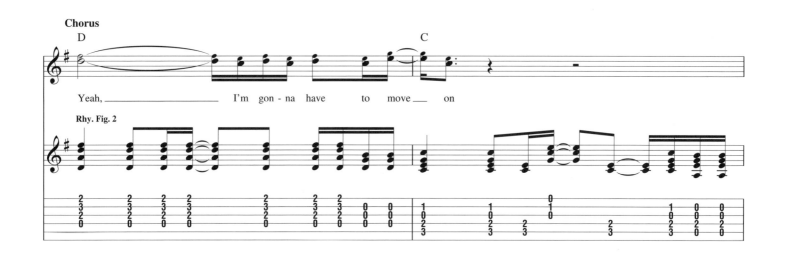

Yeah, _____ I'm gon-na have to move___ on

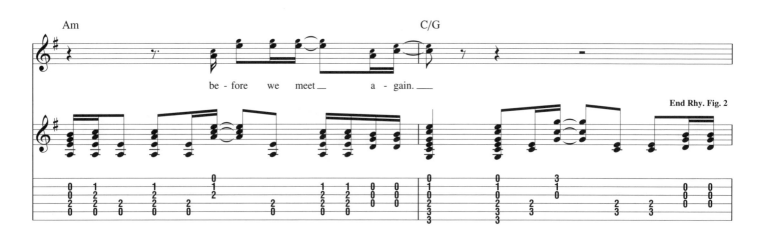

be - fore we meet___ a - gain. ___

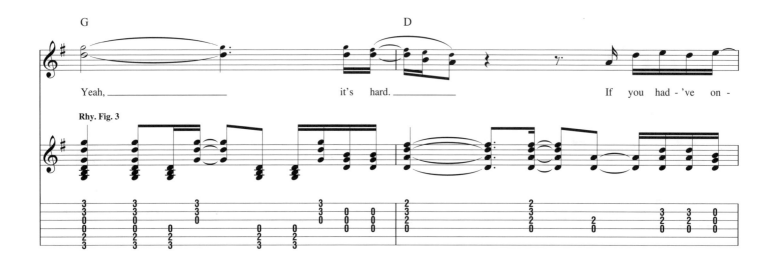

Yeah, _____ it's hard. ___ If you had - 've on -

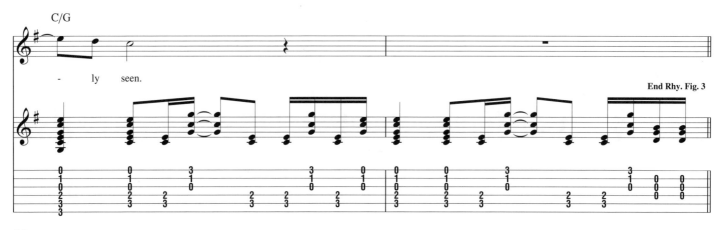

- ly seen.

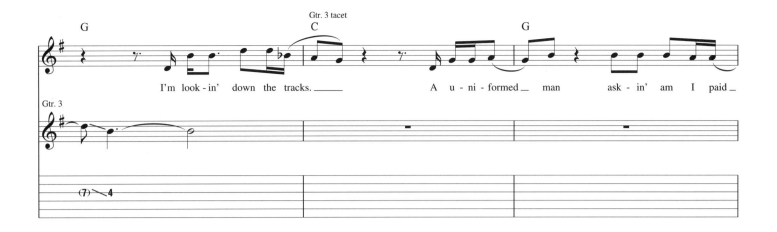

I'm look-in' down the tracks._____ A u-ni-formed__ man ask-in' am I paid__

__ up. Why would I wan-na be_____ that?_____

Chorus

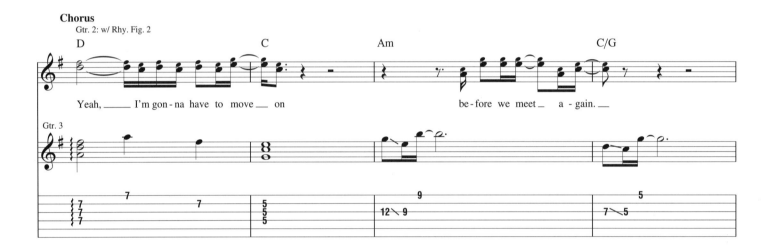

Yeah,___ I'm gon-na have to move__ on be-fore we meet__ a-gain.___

Yeah,_____ it's hard._____ If you had-'ve on-

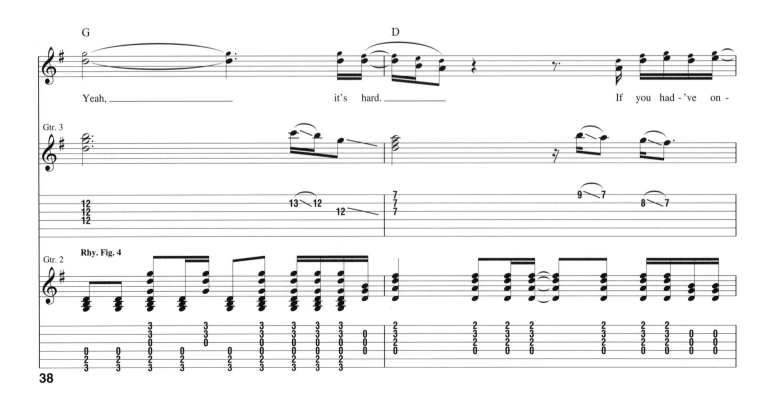

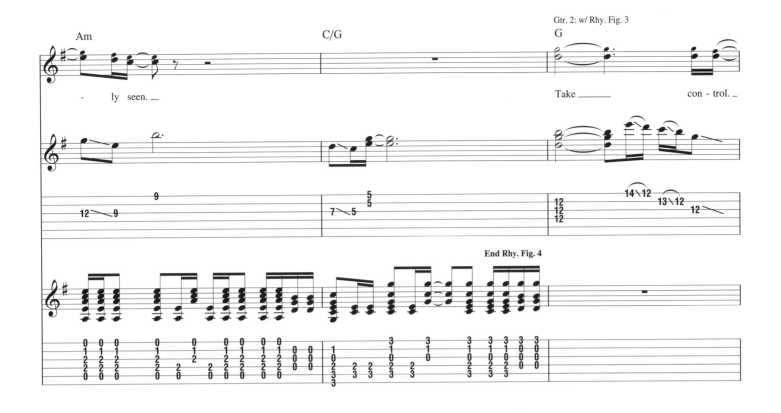

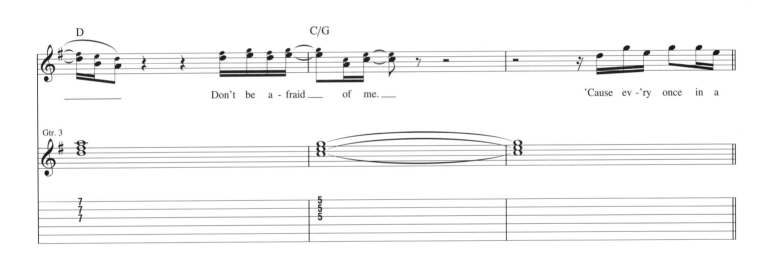

You should be hap-py just to be   a - live. ___   And just   be - cause ___

___   you just don't feel   like   com - in'   home _____

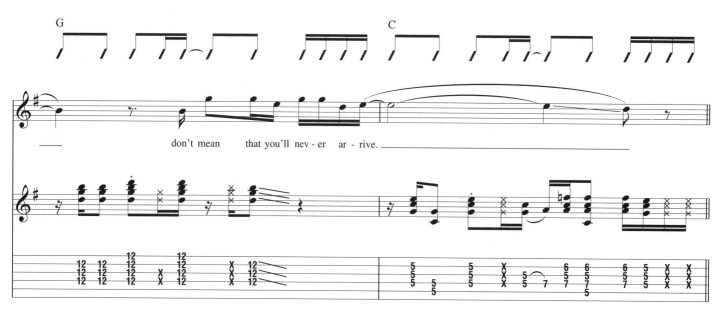

___   don't mean   that you'll nev - er   ar - rive. _____

Chorus

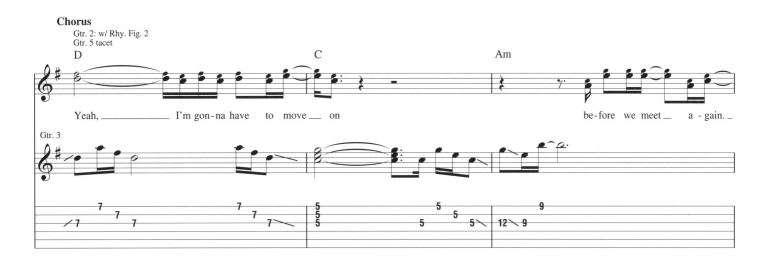

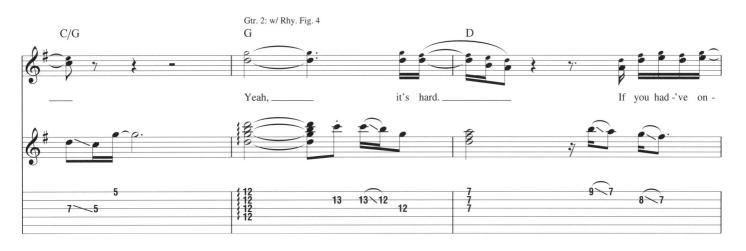

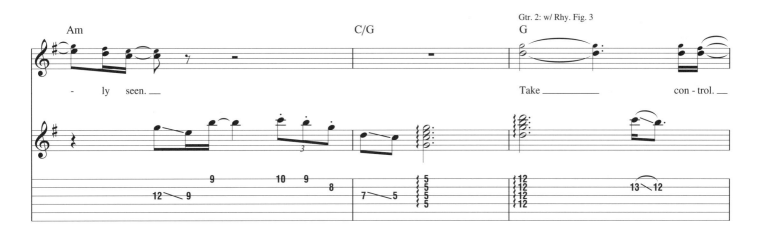

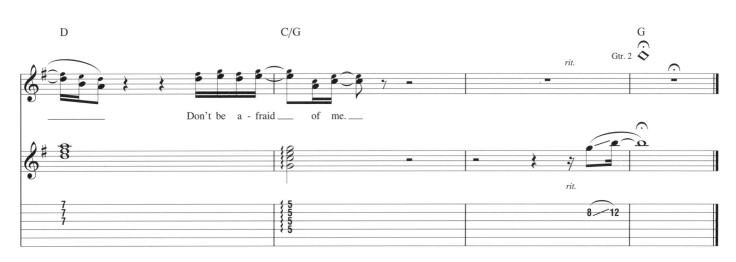

Radio Song

Words and Music by Nic Cester, Chris Cester and Cameron Muncey

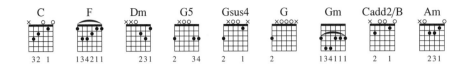

Verse

2nd time, Gtrs. 4 & 5: w/ Rhy. Fills 1 & 1A

Gtr. 1 (acous.)

mf

1. Take a look ___ at what I took, ___ a

you all know ___ of the em - per - or's clothes ___

*Gtr. 2

mf

let ring throughout

*Piano arr. for gtr.

leaf out ___ of ev - 'ry - bod - y's ___ book. ___ We see ___ what

walk - ing ___ down an emp - ty ___ road. ___ We see ___ what

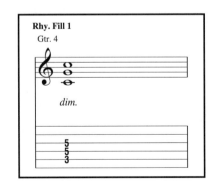

Rhy. Fill 1

Gtr. 4

dim.

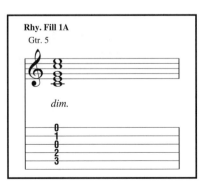

Rhy. Fill 1A

Gtr. 5

dim.

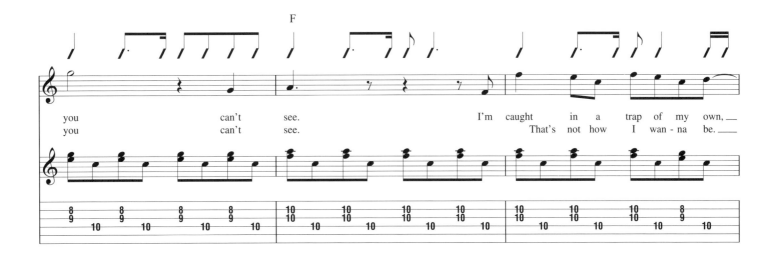

you _____ can't see.
you _____ can't see. I'm caught in a trap of my own, ___
That's not how I wan-na be. ___

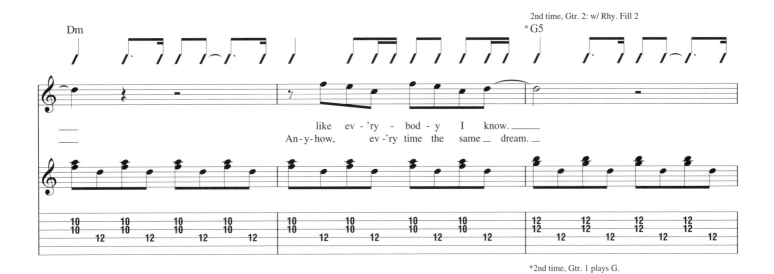

2nd time, Gtr. 2: w/ Rhy. Fill 2

*G5

___ like ev-'ry-bod-y I know. ___
___ An-y-how, ev-'ry time the same ___ dream. ___

*2nd time, Gtr. 1 plays G.

Chorus

Gsus4   G   C

Gtrs. 1 & 2 tacet

N.C.

This won't be played ___ on your ra-di-o ___ to - night. ___

Riff A
Gtr. 3 (elec.)

f

w/ fuzz & **gated amp tremolo
grad. bend

**Tremolo set for sixteenth-note regeneration.

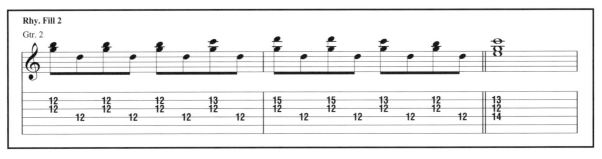

Rhy. Fill 2
Gtr. 2

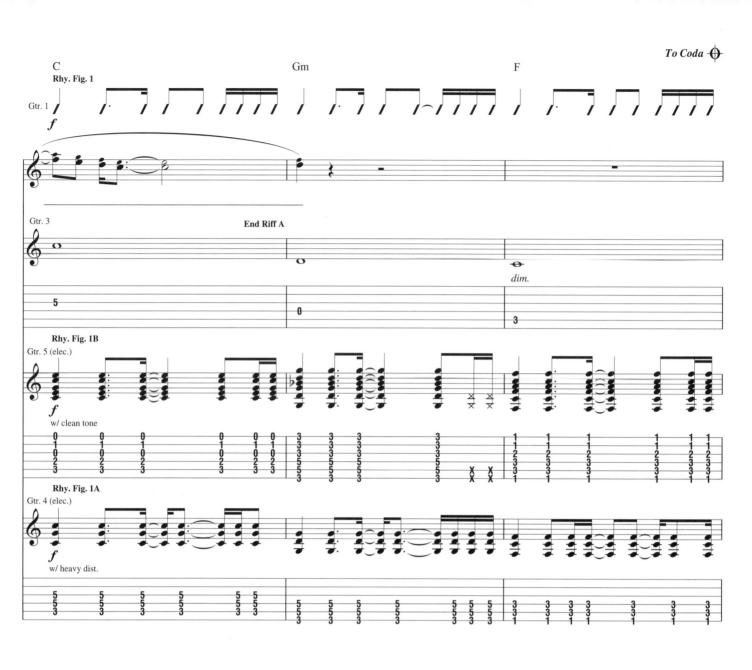

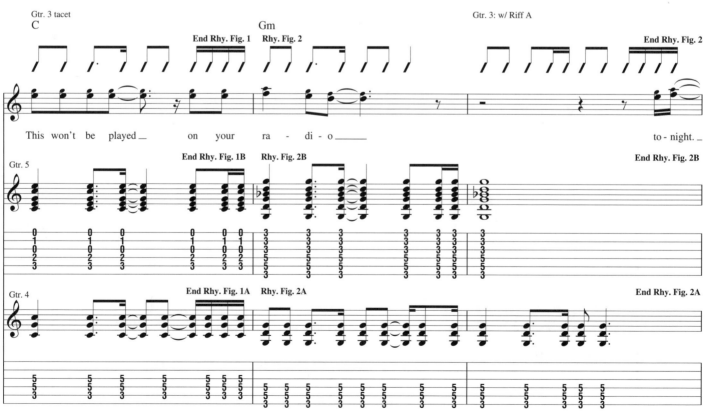

This won't be played __ on your ra - di - o __ to - night. __

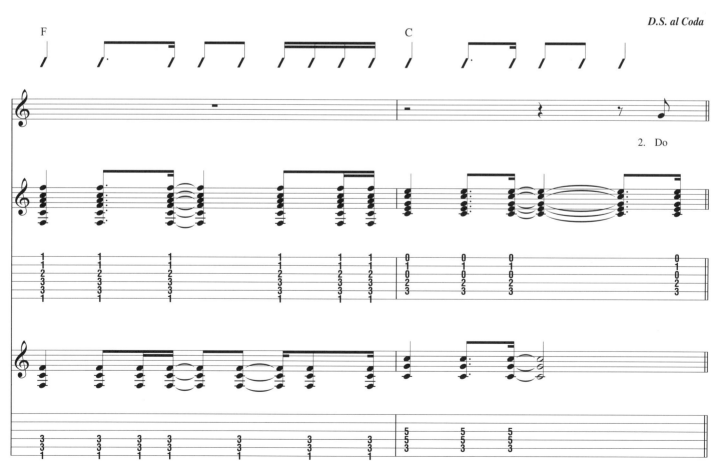

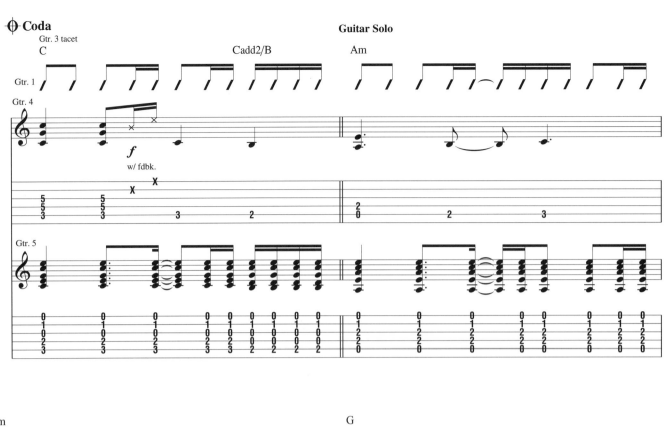

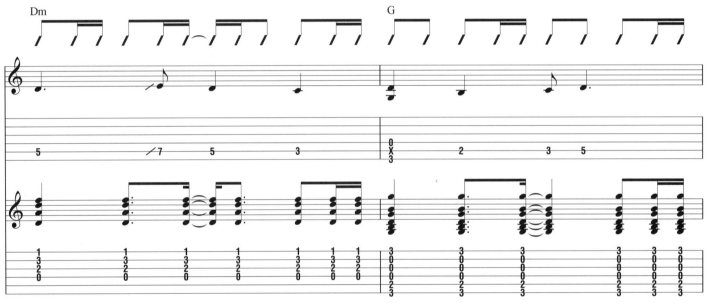

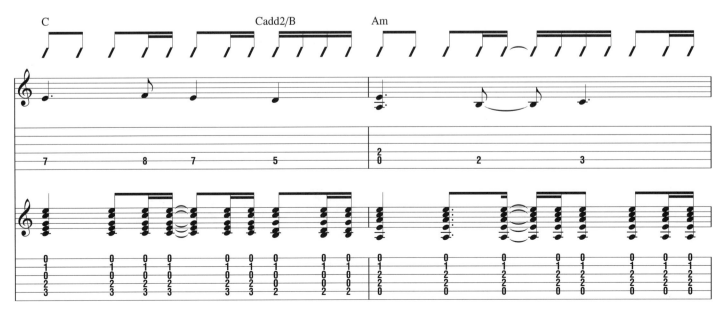

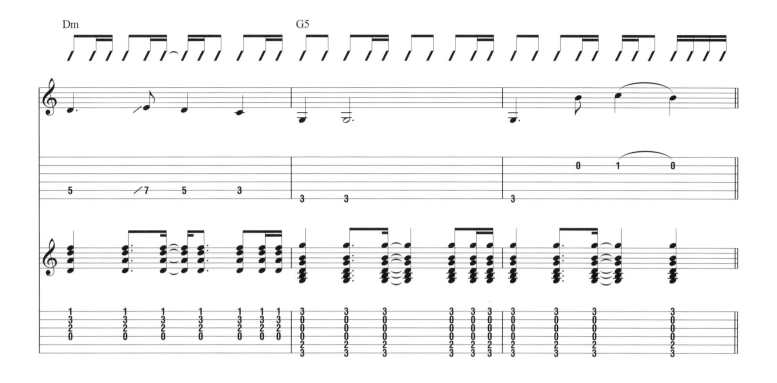

Chorus

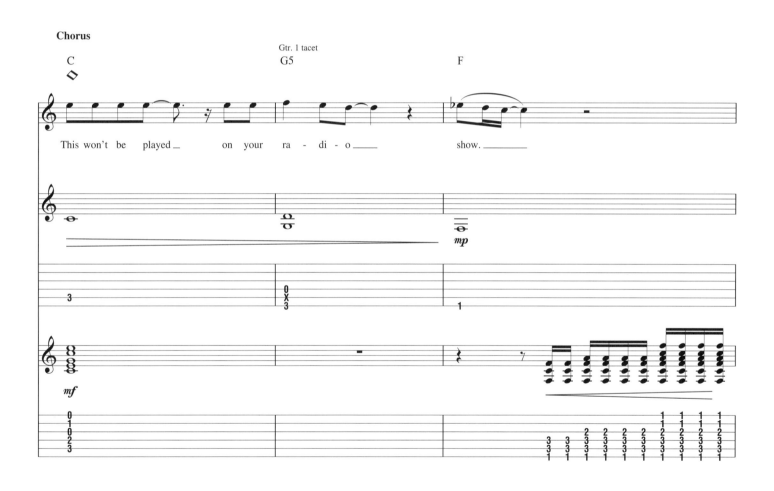

This won't be played ___ on your ra-di-o ___ show. ___

This won't be played ___ on your ra-di-o ___ to-night. ___

Outro

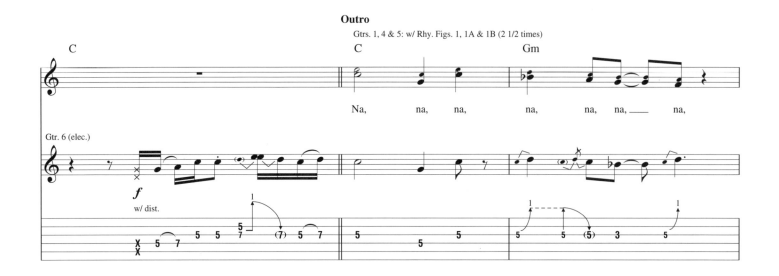

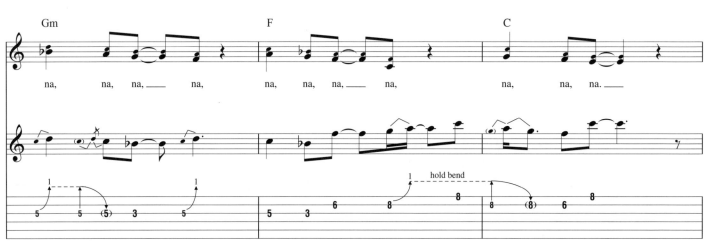

Na,   na,   na,   na,   na,   na, _____ na,

na,   na,   na, _____ na,   na.

Get Me Outta Here

Words and Music by Nic Cester and Chris Cester

A

Intro
Moderately fast Rock ♩ = 140

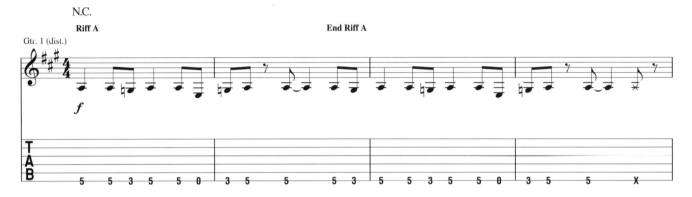

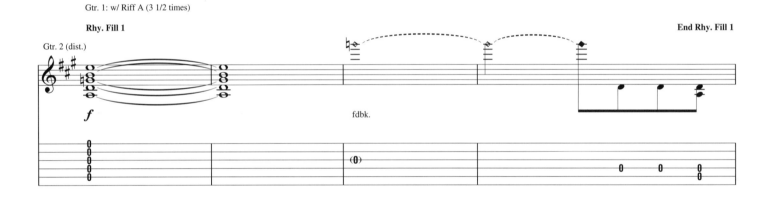

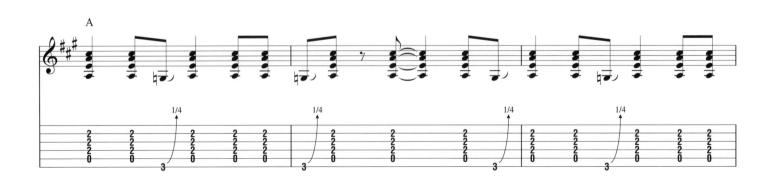

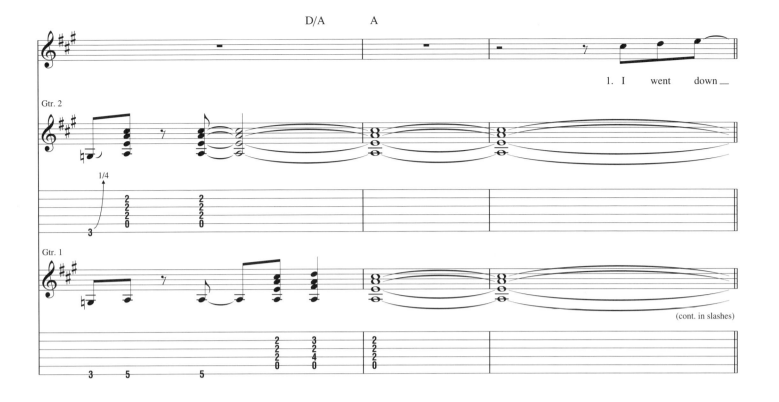

Verse

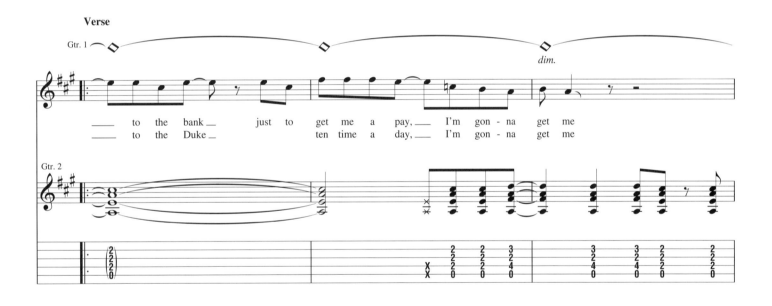

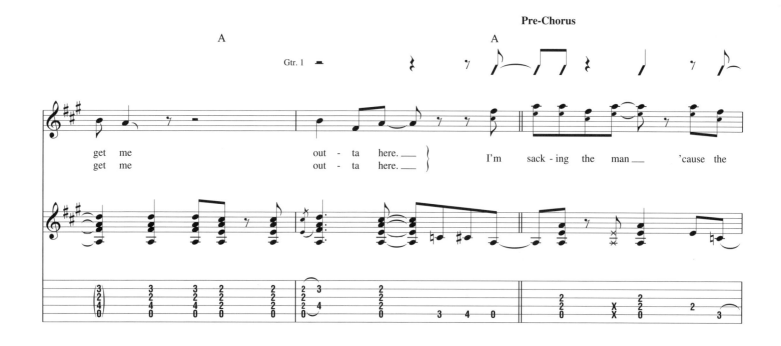

get me   out - ta here. ___   I'm sack - ing the man ___   'cause the
get me   out - ta here. ___

man   is   a   thief. ___   I'm

kick - ing the plan ___ be - fore the plan kicks   me.   I'm gon - na

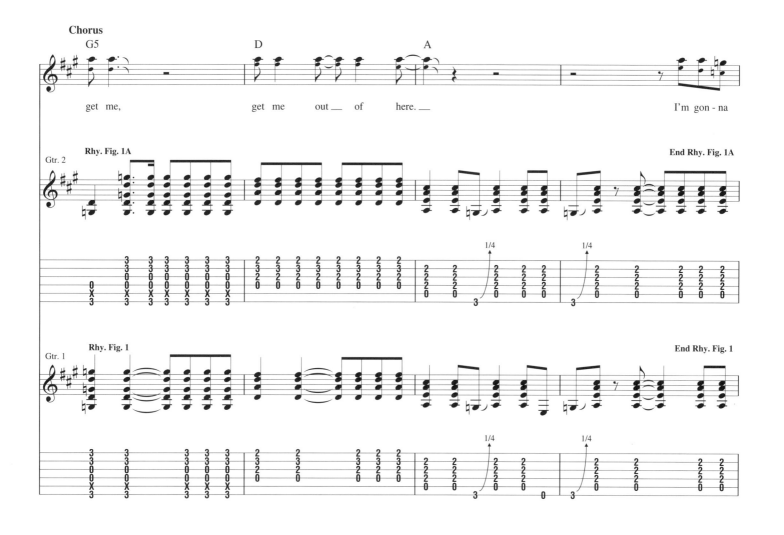

get me, get me out __ of here. __   I'm gon - na

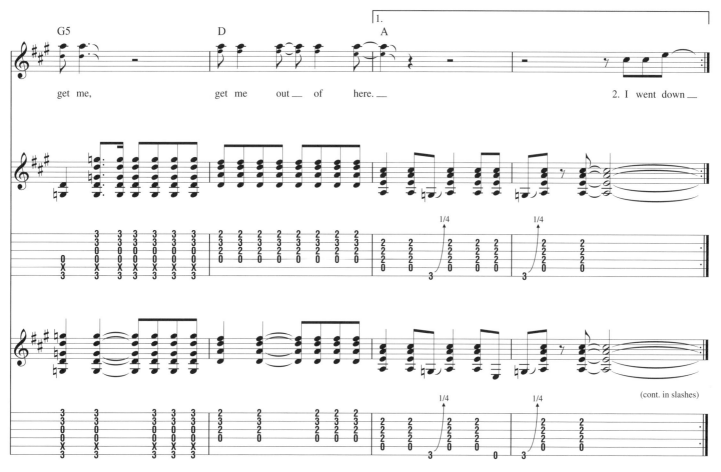

get me, get me out __ of here. __   2. I went down __

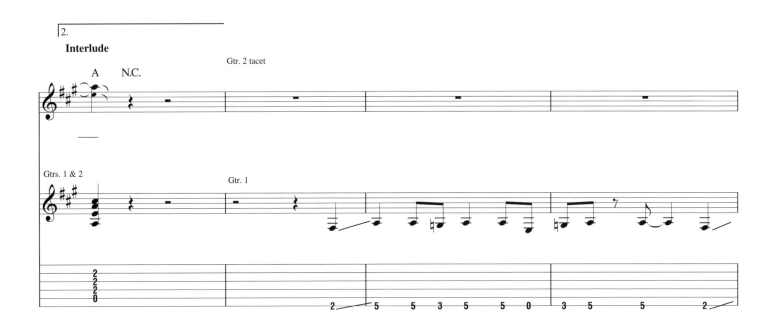

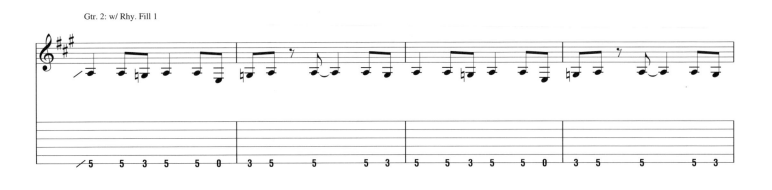

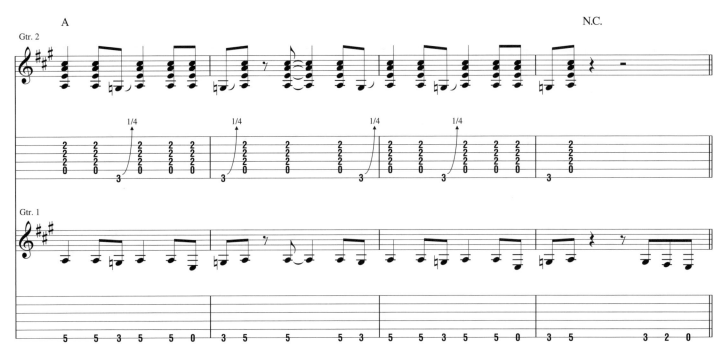

Bridge

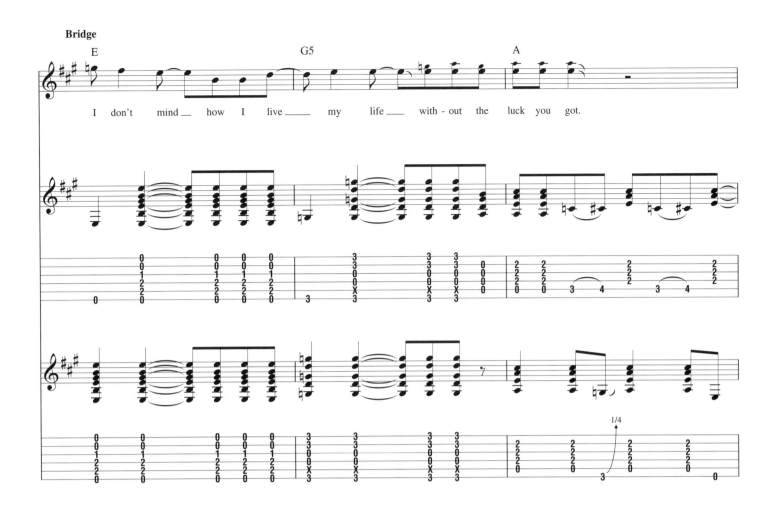

I don't mind ___ how I live ___ my life ___ with - out the luck you got.

But I ain't try'n' ___ to keep in time, ___ so just keep

off of my ride.   You won't hang___ your rust -

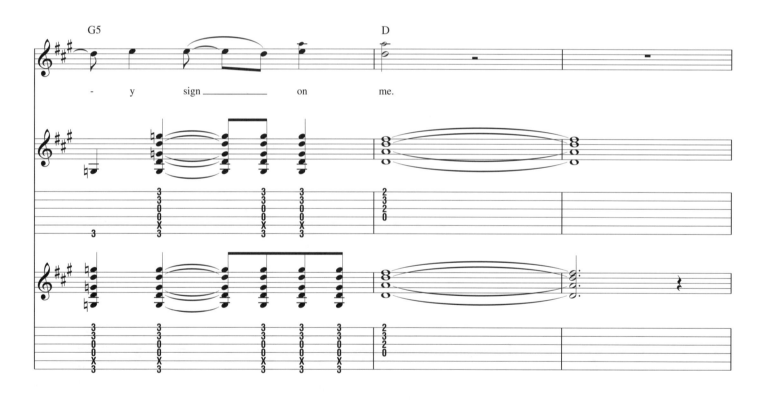

- y   sign_____ on   me.

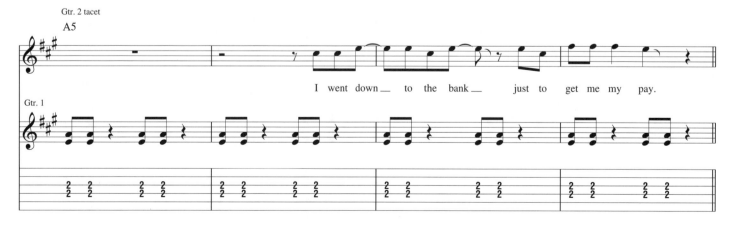

Gtr. 2 tacet

I went down___ to the bank___   just to   get me my   pay.

Gtr. 1

Chorus
Gtrs. 1 & 2: w/ Rhy. Figs. 1 & 1A (3 3/4 times)

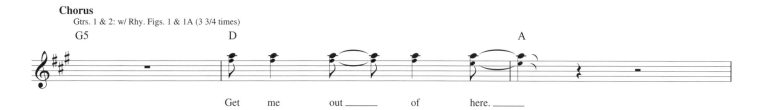

Get me out ____ of here. ____

I'm gon - na get me, get me out ____ of here, ____

____ yeah. ____ I'm gon - na get me,

get me out ____ of here. ____ I'm gon - na

get me, get me out ____ of here. ____

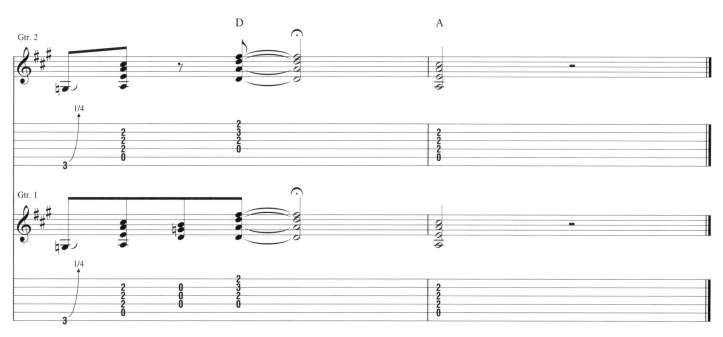

Cold Hard Bitch

Words and Music by Nic Cester, Chris Cester and Cameron Muncey

Intro
Moderate Rock ♩ = 126

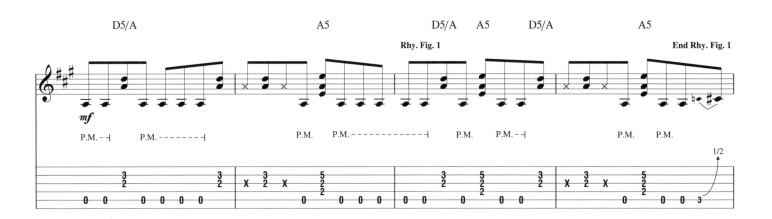

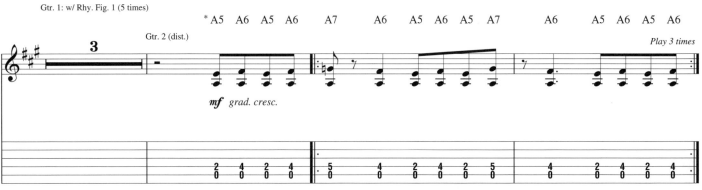

*Chord symbols refer to Gtr. 2 only.

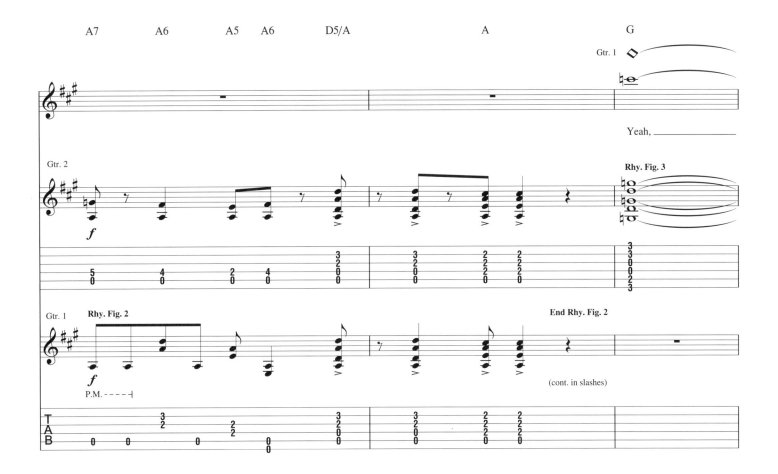

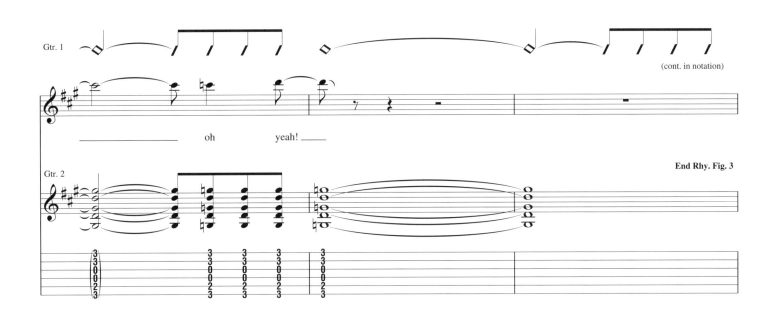

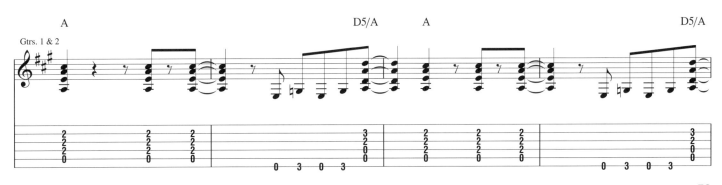

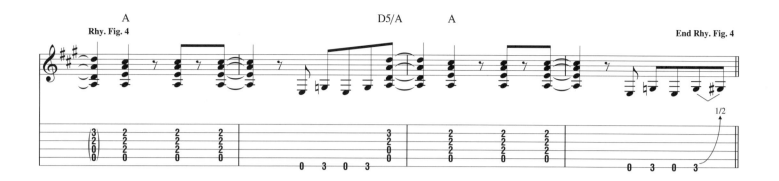

Verse

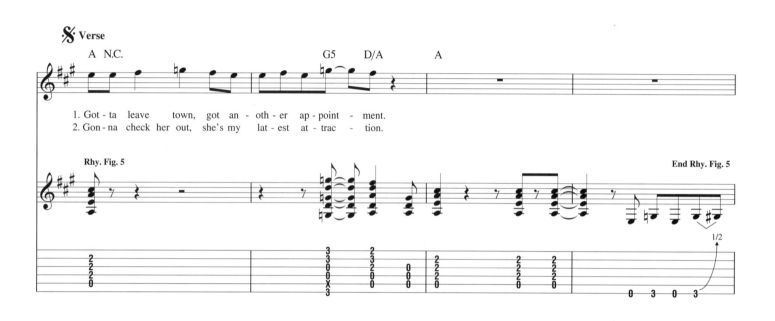

1. Got - ta leave town, got an - oth - er ap - point - ment.
2. Gon - na check her out, she's my lat - est at - trac - tion.

Spent all my rent, girl, you know I en - joyed_ it, yeah! _ Ain't
Gon - na hang a - round, wan - na get a re - ac - tion, yeah! _____

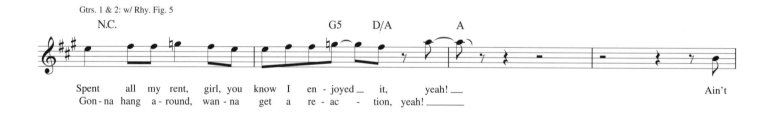

gon - na hang a - round till there's no - bod - y danc - ing. I don't wan - na hold hands and talk a -
Gon - na take her home 'cause she's o - ver ro - manc - ing. Don't wan - na hold hands and talk a -

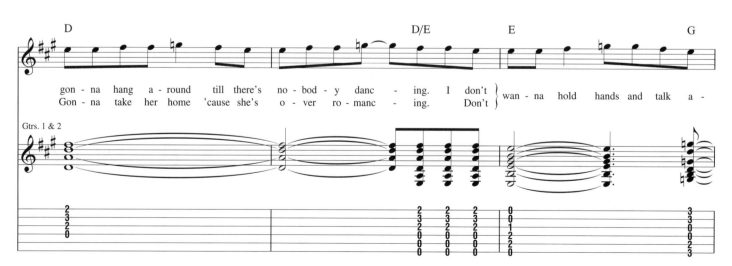

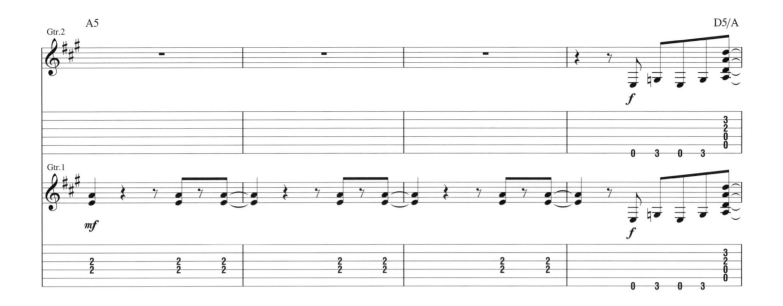

D.S. al Coda

Gtrs. 1 & 2: w/ Rhy. Fig. 4

Coda

Gtrs. 1 & 2: w/ Rhy. Fig. 6

Cold hard bitch, __ she was shak-in' her hips, __ well, that was all that I need. __ I'm

Gtrs. 1 & 2: w/ Rhy. Fig. 7

wait-ing, give me. Cold hard bitch. __ Just a kiss on the lips __ and I was on my knees. __

Bridge

Yeah, __ I'm wait - ing.   Yeah, __ I'm

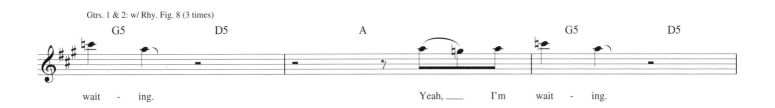

wait - ing.   Yeah, ___ I'm wait - ing.

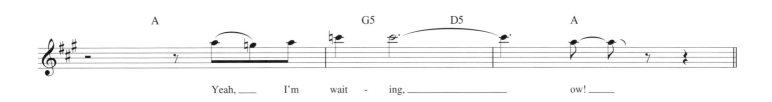

Yeah, ___ I'm wait - ing, _____ ow! ___

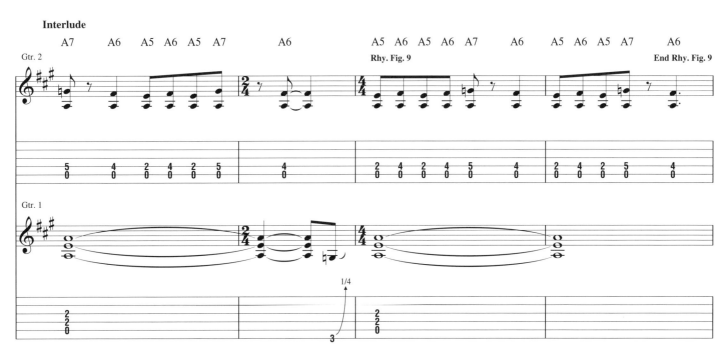

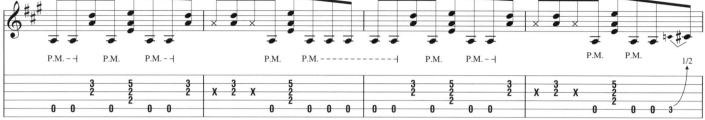

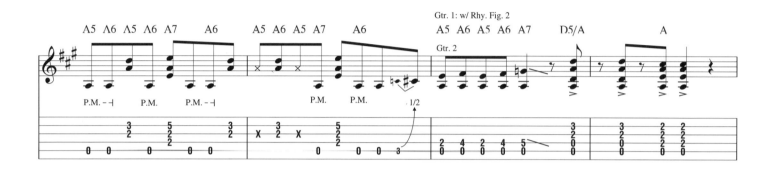

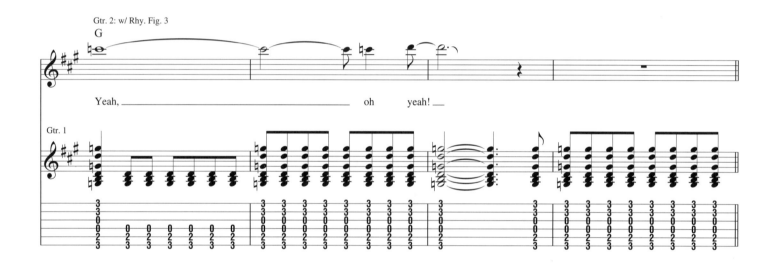

Chorus

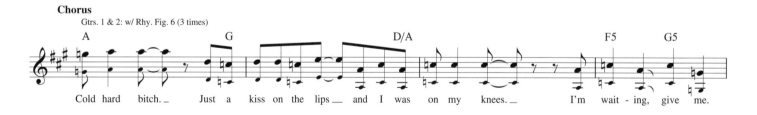

Cold hard bitch.__ Just a kiss on the lips__ and I was on my knees.__ I'm wait-ing, give me.

Cold hard bitch,_ she was shak-in' her hips,_ well, that was all that I need._ I'm wait-ing, give me.

Cold hard bitch._ Just a kiss on the lips__ and I was on my knees._ I'm wait-ing, give me.

Come Around Again

Words and Music by Nic Cester and Cameron Muncey

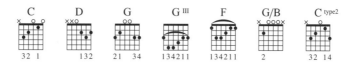

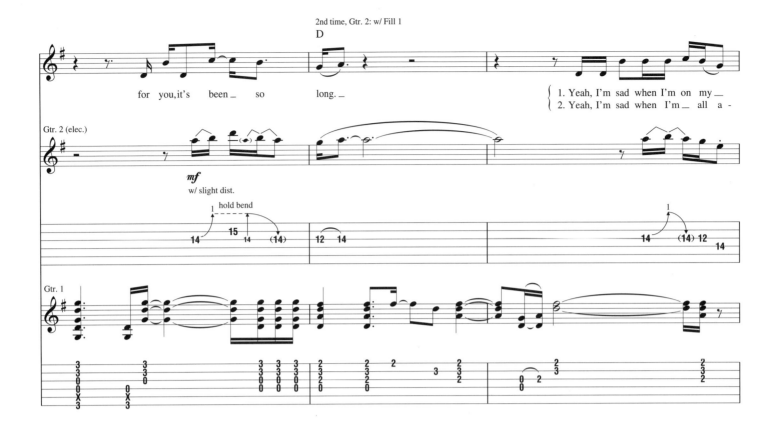

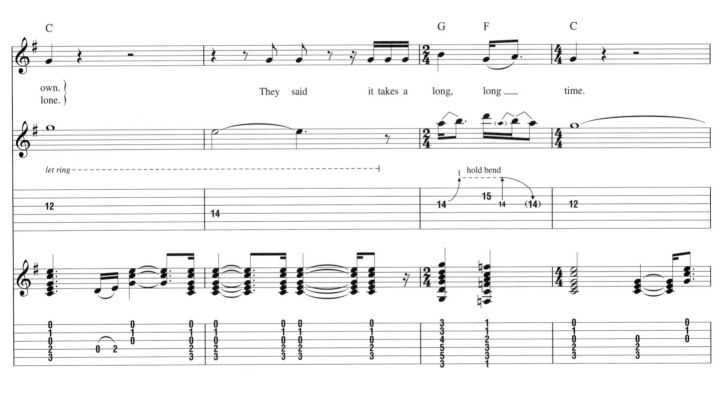

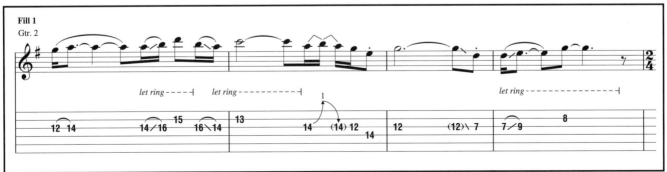

2nd time, Gtr. 2: w/ Fill 2

If it's not too _ much could you hear me _____ now? You

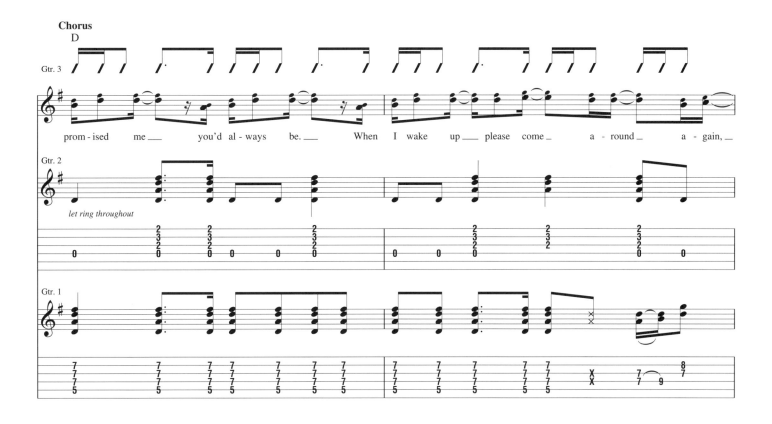

Chorus

Gtr. 3

prom - ised me _ you'd al - ways be. When I wake up _ please come _ a - round _ a - gain, _

Gtr. 2

let ring throughout

Gtr. 1

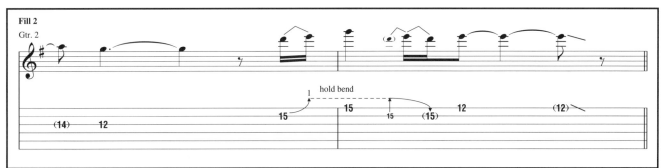

Fill 2

Gtr. 2

hold bend

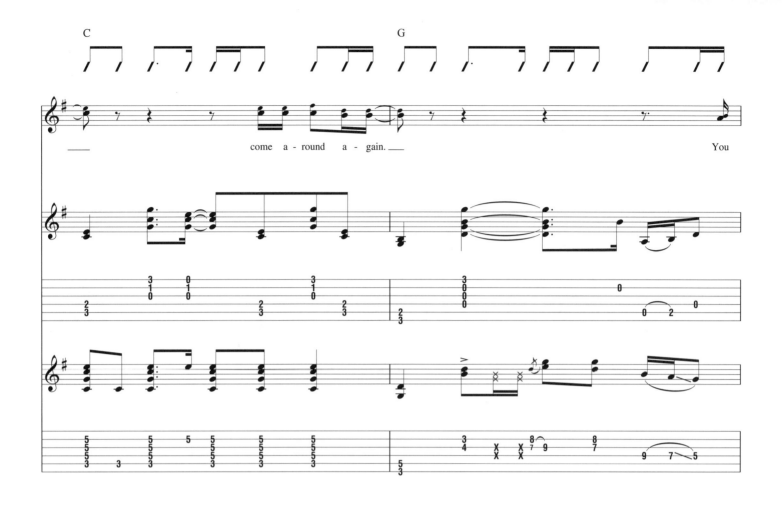

come a - round a - gain. ___ You

prom-ised me ___ you'd al - ways be. ___ When I wake up ___ please come ___ a - round ___ a - gain, ___

come a-round   a - gain. ___   Yeah. ___

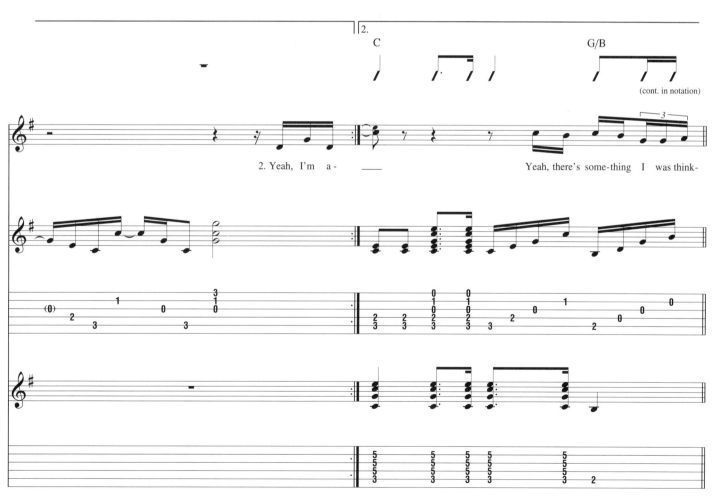

2. Yeah, I'm a- ___   Yeah, there's some-thing I was think-

(cont. in notation)

Bridge

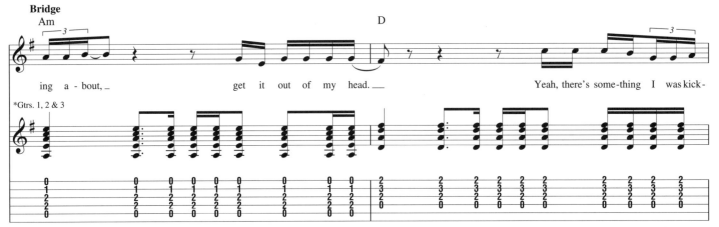

ing a - bout, __   get it out of my head. ___   Yeah, there's some-thing I was kick-

*Gtrs. 1, 2 & 3

*Composite arrangement

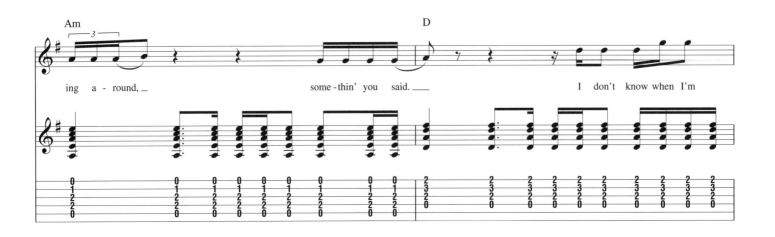

ing   a - round, __   some-thin' you   said. ___   I   don't   know when I'm

right,   I   on - ly   know when I'm   wrong.   So when you gon - na

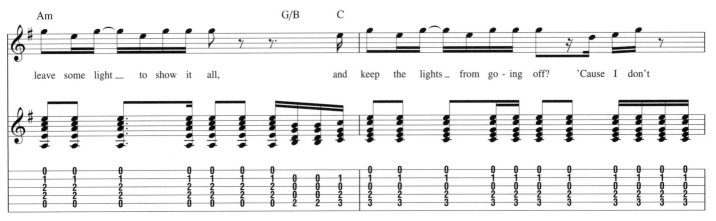

leave some light __ to show it all,   and keep the lights __ from go - ing off?   'Cause I don't

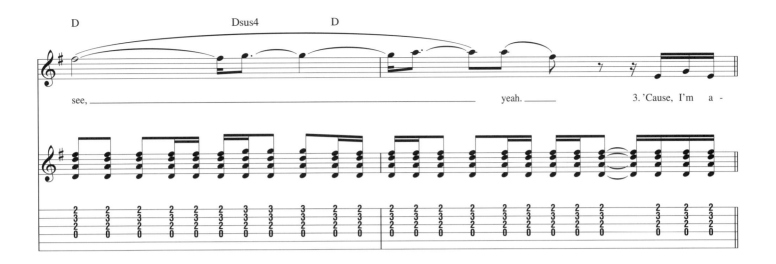

see, _____ yeah. _____ 3. 'Cause, I'm a-

Verse

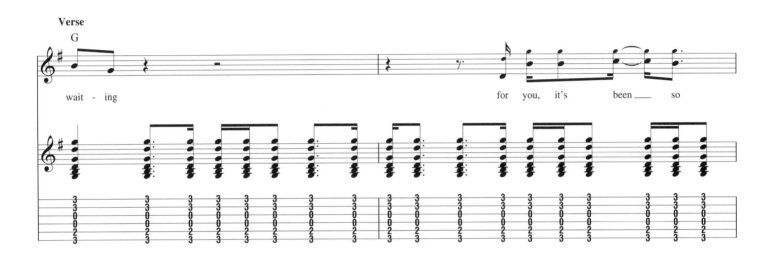

wait - ing   for you, it's   been ___ so

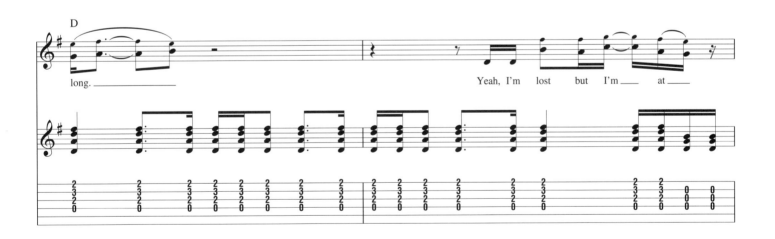

long. _____   Yeah, I'm lost but I'm ___ at ___

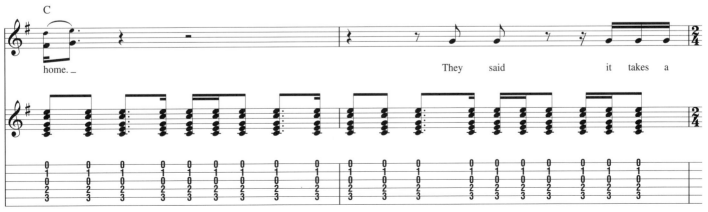

home. _   They   said   it takes a

Outro

Take It or Leave It

Words and Music by Nic Cester, Chris Cester and Cameron Muncey

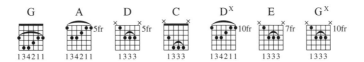

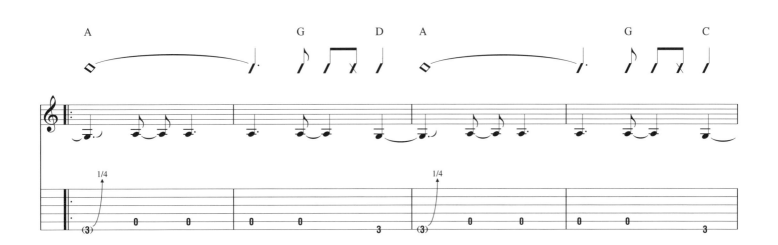

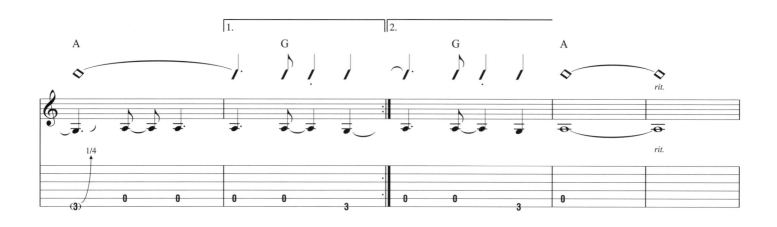

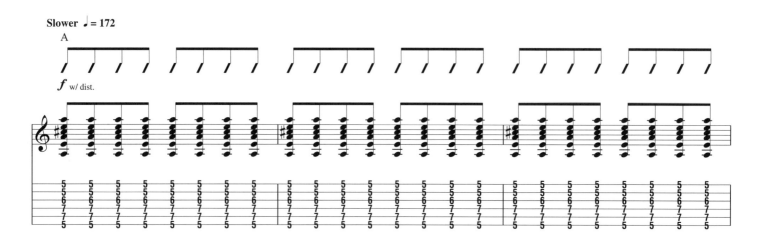

Slower ♩ = 172

Verse

2nd time, Gtr. 1: w/ Rhy. Fill 1

1. Yeah. _____ Just take it or leave it, yeah. _____
2. Yeah! _____ Just take it or leave it, yeah. _____

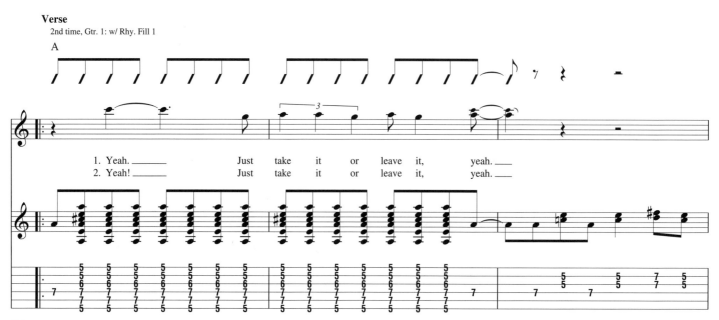

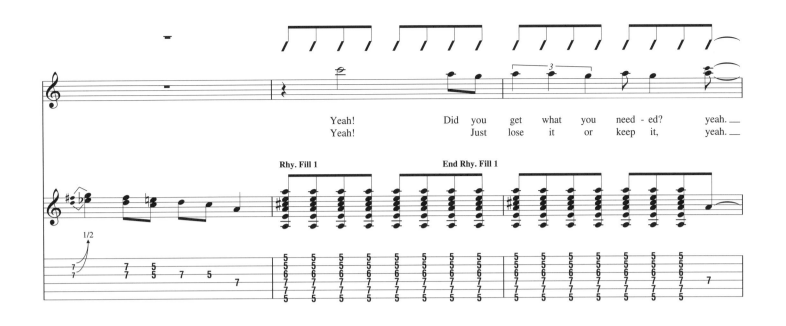

Yeah!   Did   you   get   what   you   need - ed?   yeah. __

Yeah!   Just   lose   it   or   keep   it,   yeah. __

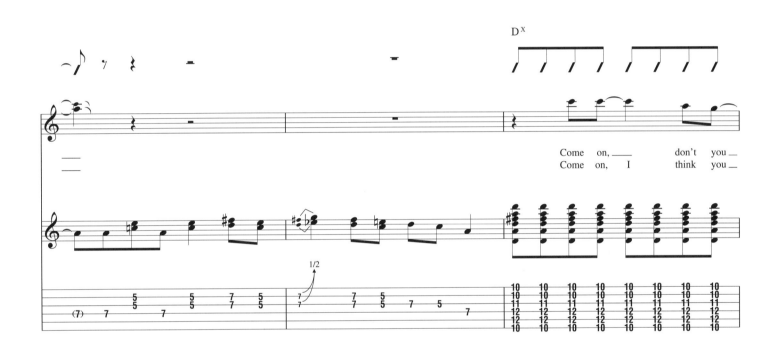

Come   on, __   don't   you __

Come   on,   I   think   you __

__ know   what   you   got   to   do? __

__ know   what   you've   got   to   do. __

A

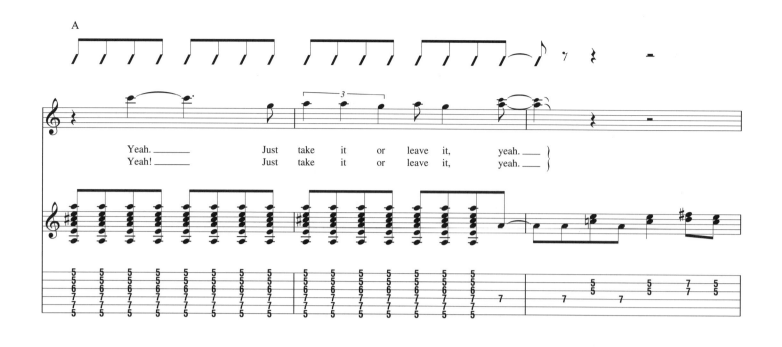

Yeah. ___ Just take it or leave it, yeah. ___
Yeah! ___ Just take it or leave it, yeah. ___

E   G^X
Rhy. Fig. 1A

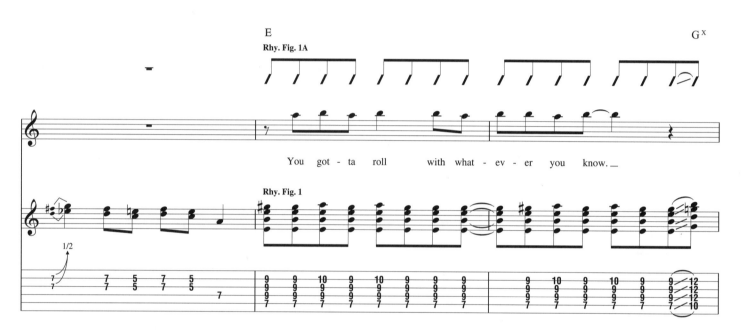

You got-ta roll with what-ev-er you know. ___

Rhy. Fig. 1

N.C.
End Rhy. Fig. 1A

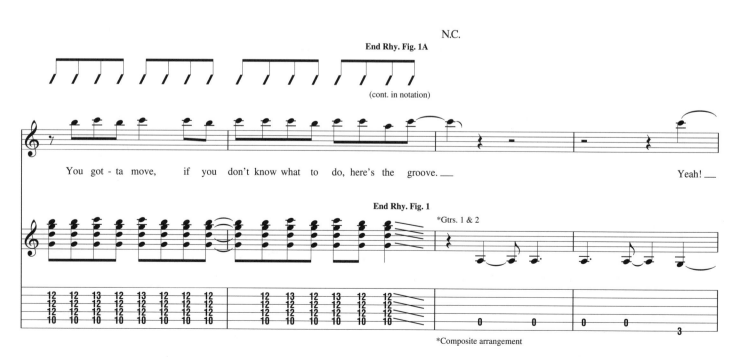

(cont. in notation)

You got-ta move, if you don't know what to do, here's the groove. ___   Yeah! ___

End Rhy. Fig. 1
*Gtrs. 1 & 2

*Composite arrangement

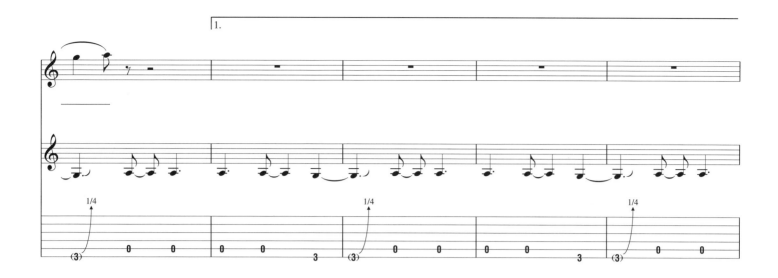

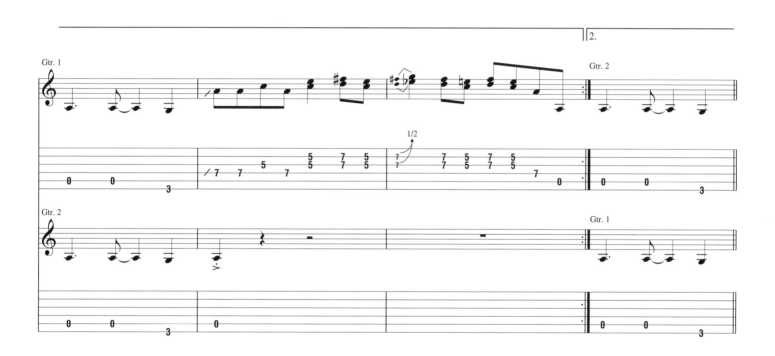

Interlude

N.C.

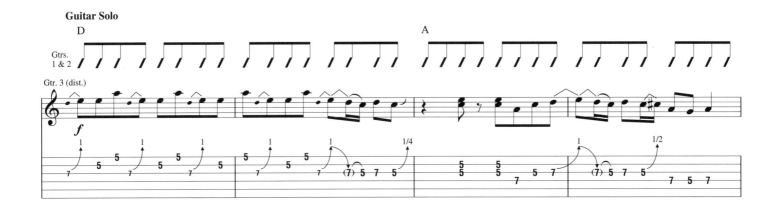

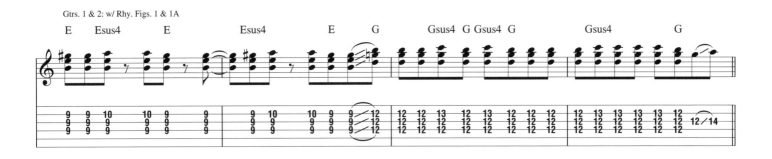

Lazy Gun

Words and Music by Nic Cester and Chris Cester

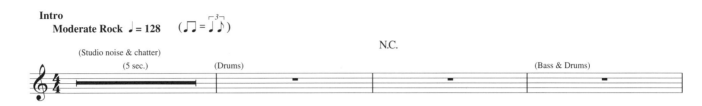

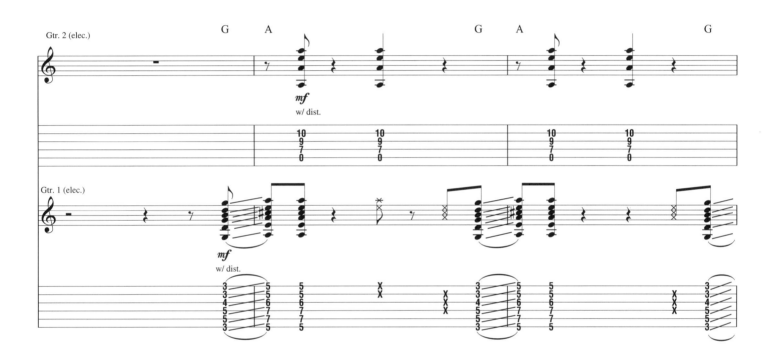

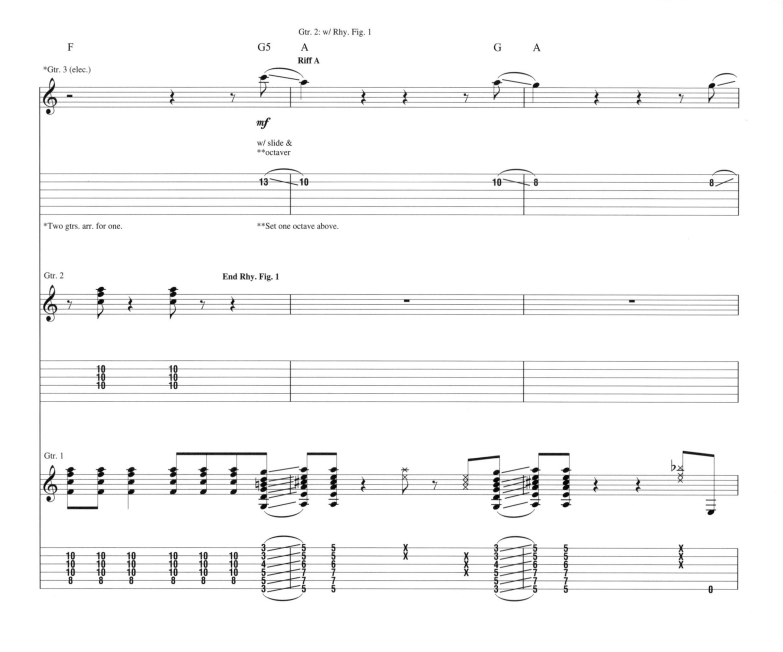

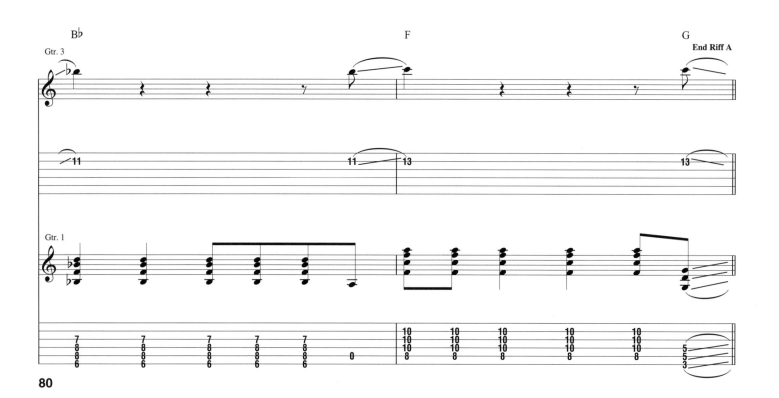

Verse

Gtr. 2: w/ Rhy. Fig. 1 (3 3/4 times)
1st time, Gtr. 3: w/ Riff A (3 3/4 times)
2nd time, Gtr. 3: w/ Fill 1
2nd time, Gtr. 4 tacet

1. La - zy gun ___ messed up ___ my tel - e - vi - sion, yeah. ___
2. La - zy gun ___ messed up ___ my tel - e - vi - sion fun. ___

Gtr. 1: w/ Rhy. Fig. 2 (2 3/4 times)
2nd time, Gtr. 3: w/ Riff A (2 3/4 times)

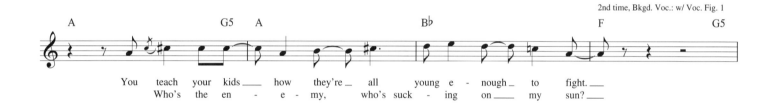

You get ___ no young - er from ___ those col - ours in ___ your hair. ___
Shoot the shot - gun but ___ the war ___ is nev - er won. ___

You teach your kids ___ how they're ___ all young e - nough ___ to fight. ___
Who's the en - e - my, who's suck - ing on ___ my sun? ___

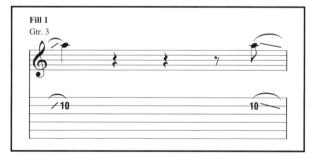

You talk a - bout ___ the an - swer, tell ___ them they're ___ al - right. ___
I'm the on - ly one ___ left now, ___ you've ta - ken all ___ my fun. ___

Fill 1
Gtr. 3

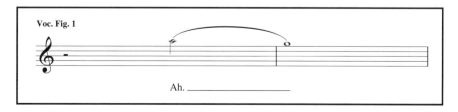

Voc. Fig. 1

Ah. ___

81

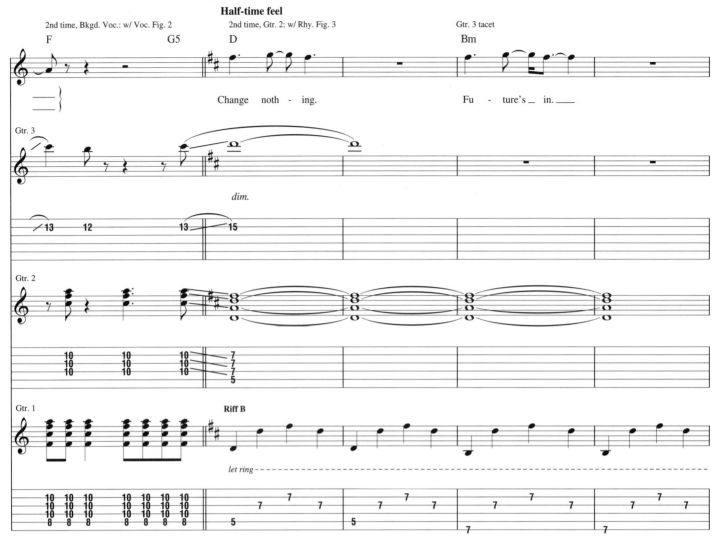

1st time, Gtr. 1: w/ Riff B (1st 6 meas.)
2nd time, Gtr. 1: w/ Riff B

*Composite arrangement

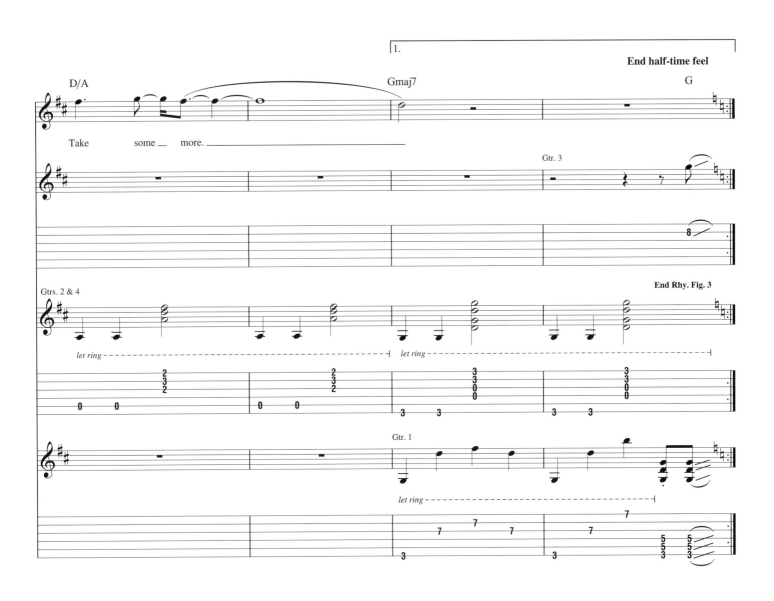

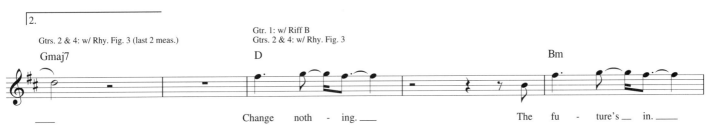

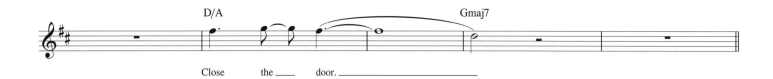

Close   the   door.

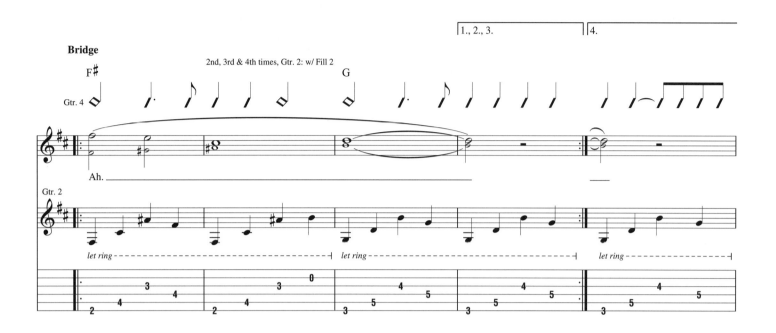

Bridge

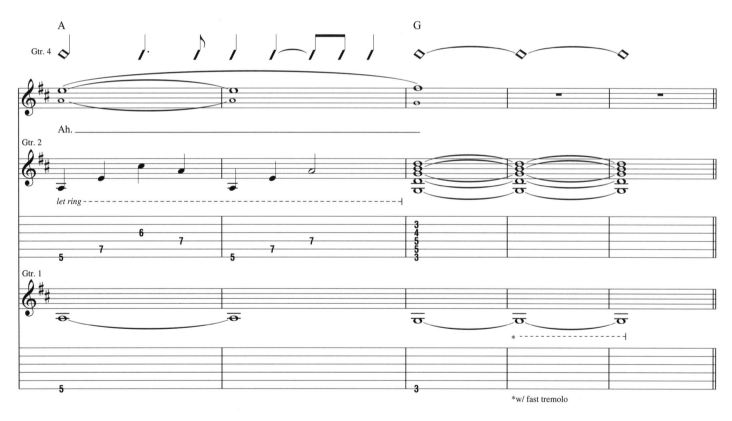

*w/ fast tremolo

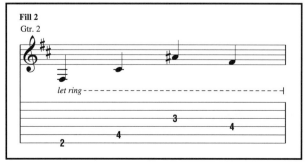

Chorus
Gtr. 2: w/ Rhy. Fig. 3 (4 times)

Change noth - ing. ____ The fu - ture's __ in. ____

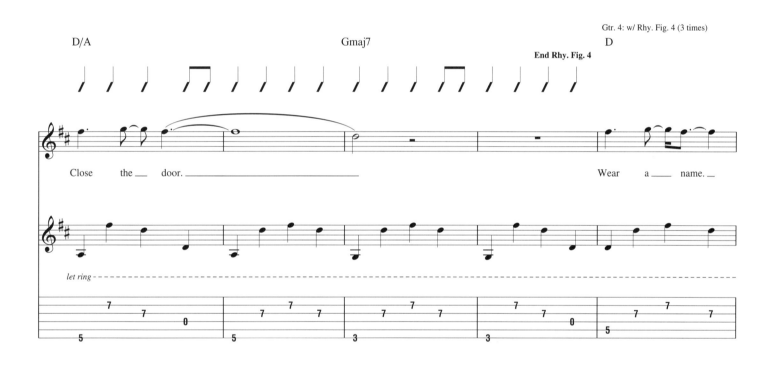

Close the __ door. ____ Wear a __ name. ____

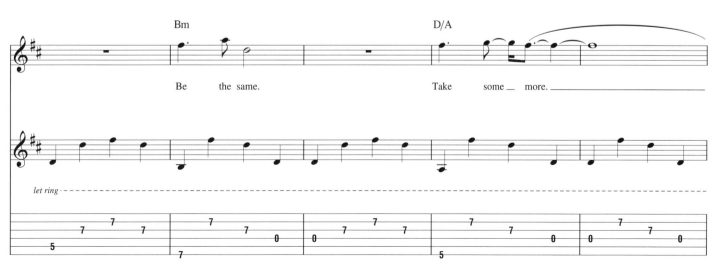

Be the same. Take some __ more. ____

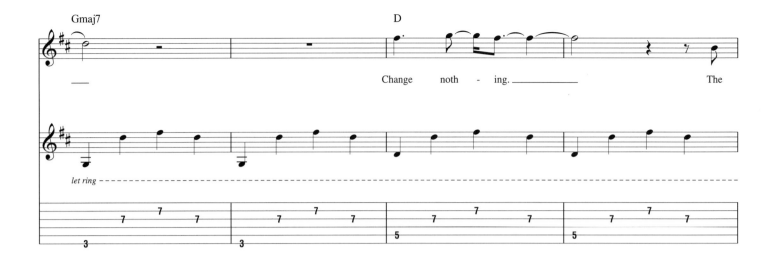

Change noth - ing. _____ The

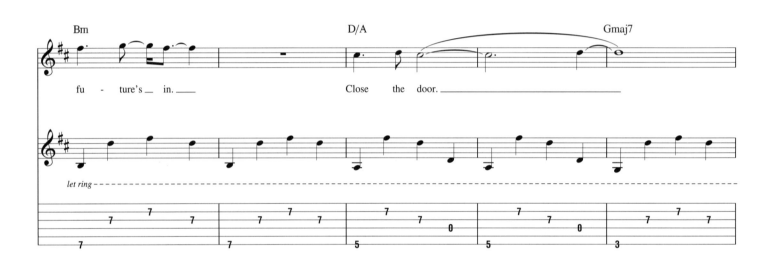

fu - ture's _ in. _____ Close the door. _____

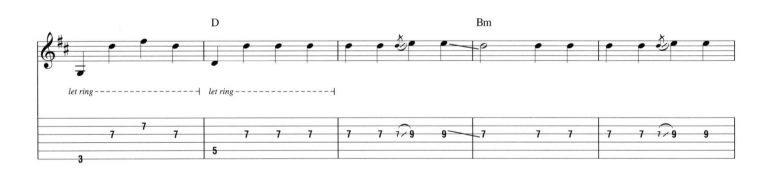

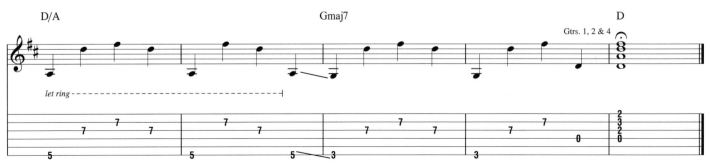

Timothy

Words and Music by Chris Cester

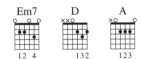

Tim - o - thy, _____ we found _____ your space - ship. Tim - o - thy, it's the far -

Gtr. 2
(elec.)

Riff A

mf

w/ clean tone & tremolo

let ring throughout

Gtr. 1

- thest you've _ ev - er flown. ___

Nev - er used _

your head ___ to find out what ___ this whole ___ thing meant. ___

End Rhy. Fig. 1

(cont. in slashes)

Chorus

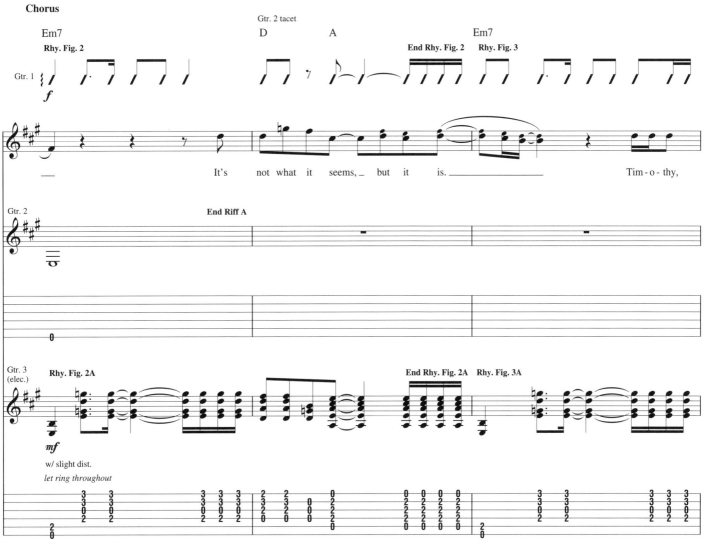

It's not what it seems, ___ but it is. ___ Tim-o-thy,

Gtr. 2 tacet

Em7   D   A   Em7

Rhy. Fig. 2   **End Rhy. Fig. 2**   **Rhy. Fig. 3**

Gtr. 1   *f*

Gtr. 2   **End Riff A**

Gtr. 3 (elec.)   **Rhy. Fig. 2A**   **End Rhy. Fig. 2A**   **Rhy. Fig. 3A**

mf

w/ slight dist.

let ring throughout

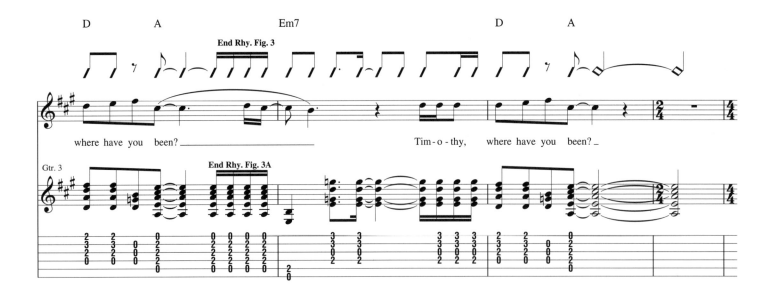

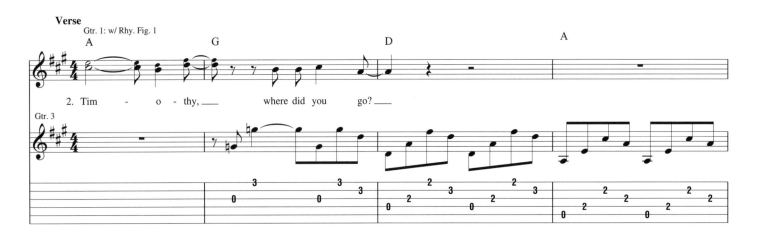

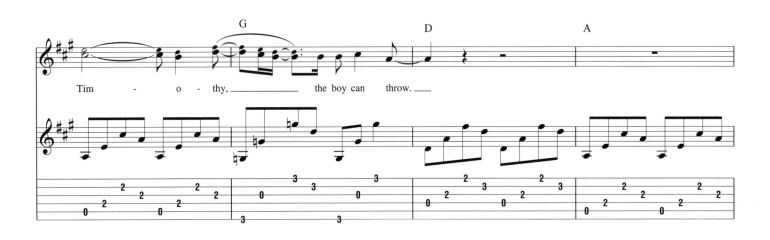

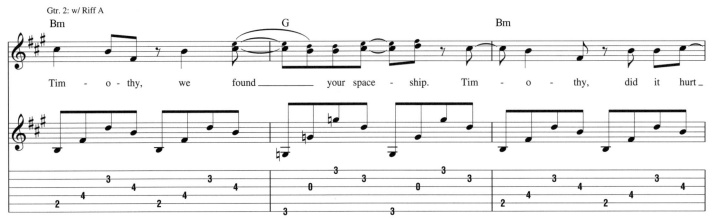

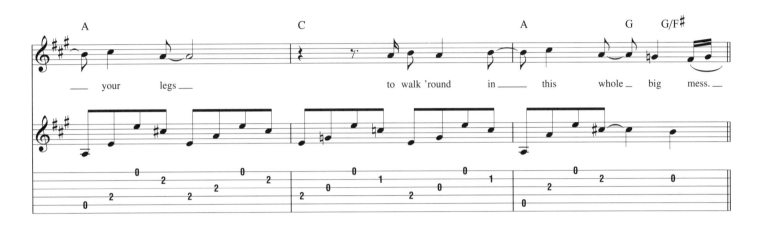

Chorus

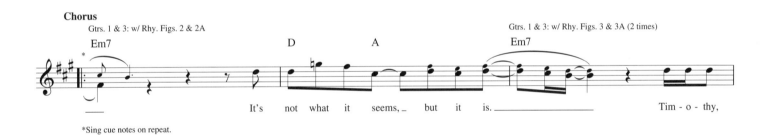

*Sing cue notes on repeat.

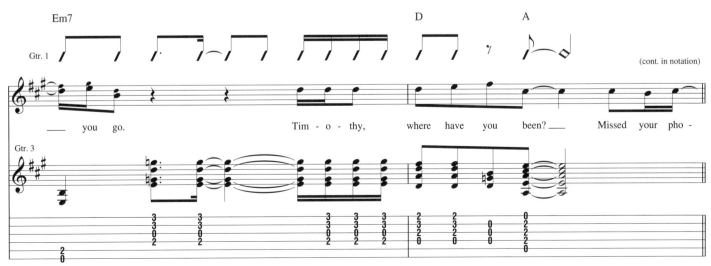

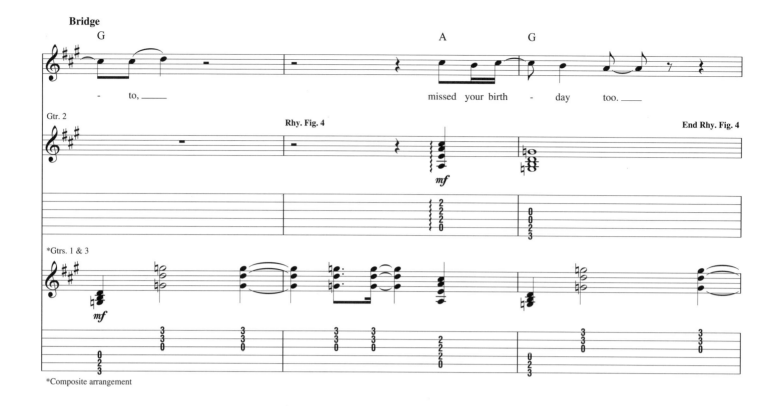

- to, _____

missed your birth - day too. _____

*Composite arrangement

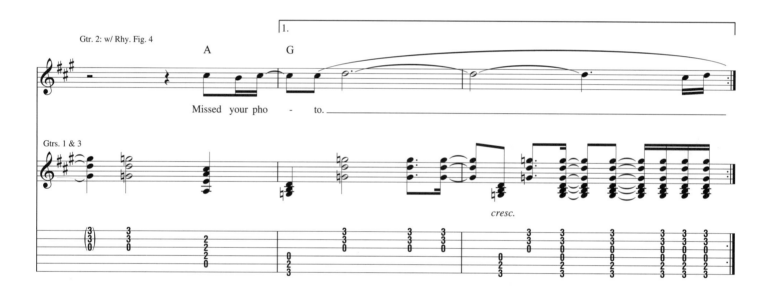

Missed your pho - to. _____

cresc.

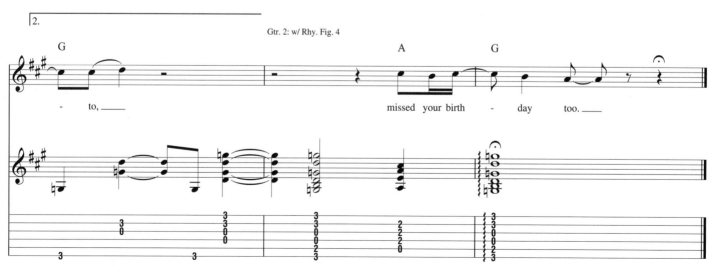

- to, _____

missed your birth - day too. _____

Guitar Notation Legend

Guitar Music can be notated three different ways: on a *musical staff*, in *tablature*, and in *rhythm slashes*.

RHYTHM SLASHES are written above the staff. Strum chords in the rhythm indicated. Use the chord diagrams found at the top of the first page of the transcription for the appropriate chord voicings. Round noteheads indicate single notes.

THE MUSICAL STAFF shows pitches and rhythms and is divided by bar lines into measures. Pitches are named after the first seven letters of the alphabet.

TABLATURE graphically represents the guitar fingerboard. Each horizontal line represents a a string, and each number represents a fret.

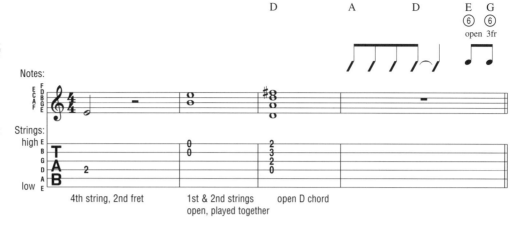

4th string, 2nd fret   1st & 2nd strings open, played together   open D chord

Definitions for Special Guitar Notation

HALF-STEP BEND: Strike the note and bend up 1/2 step.

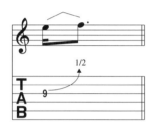

WHOLE-STEP BEND: Strike the note and bend up one step.

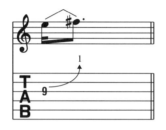

GRACE NOTE BEND: Strike the note and immediately bend up as indicated.

SLIGHT (MICROTONE) BEND: Strike the note and bend up 1/4 step.

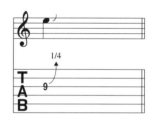

BEND AND RELEASE: Strike the note and bend up as indicated, then release back to the original note. Only the first note is struck.

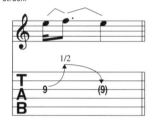

PRE-BEND: Bend the note as indicated, then strike it.

PRE-BEND AND RELEASE: Bend the note as indicated. Strike it and release the bend back to the original note.

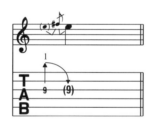

UNISON BEND: Strike the two notes simultaneously and bend the lower note up to the pitch of the higher.

VIBRATO: The string is vibrated by rapidly bending and releasing the note with the fretting hand.

WIDE VIBRATO: The pitch is varied to a greater degree by vibrating with the fretting hand.

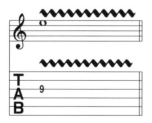

HAMMER-ON: Strike the first (lower) note with one finger, then sound the higher note (on the same string) with another finger by fretting it without picking.

PULL-OFF: Place both fingers on the notes to be sounded. Strike the first note and without picking, pull the finger off to sound the second (lower) note.

LEGATO SLIDE: Strike the first note and then slide the same fret-hand finger up or down to the second note. The second note is not struck.

SHIFT SLIDE: Same as legato slide, except the second note is struck.

TRILL: Very rapidly alternate between the notes indicated by continuously hammering on and pulling off.

TAPPING: Hammer ("tap") the fret indicated with the pick-hand index or middle finger and pull off to the note fretted by the fret hand.

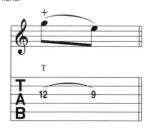

NATURAL HARMONIC: Strike the note while the fret-hand lightly touches the string directly over the fret indicated.

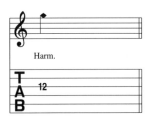

PINCH HARMONIC: The note is fretted normally and a harmonic is produced by adding the edge of the thumb or the tip of the index finger of the pick hand to the normal pick attack.

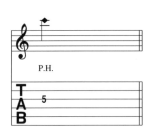

HARP HARMONIC: The note is fretted normally and a harmonic is produced by gently resting the pick hand's index finger directly above the indicated fret (in parentheses) while the pick hand's thumb or pick assists by plucking the appropriate string.

PICK SCRAPE: The edge of the pick is rubbed down (or up) the string, producing a scratchy sound.

MUFFLED STRINGS: A percussive sound is produced by laying the fret hand across the string(s) without depressing, and striking them with the pick hand.

PALM MUTING: The note is partially muted by the pick hand lightly touching the string(s) just before the bridge.

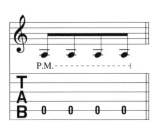

RAKE: Drag the pick across the strings indicated with a single motion.

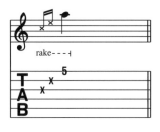

TREMOLO PICKING: The note is picked as rapidly and continuously as possible.

ARPEGGIATE: Play the notes of the chord indicated by quickly rolling them from bottom to top.

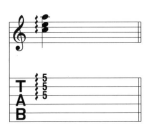

VIBRATO BAR DIVE AND RETURN: The pitch of the note or chord is dropped a specified number of steps (in rhythm) then returned to the original pitch.

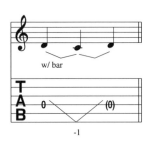

VIBRATO BAR SCOOP: Depress the bar just before striking the note, then quickly release the bar.

VIBRATO BAR DIP: Strike the note and then immediately drop a specified number of steps, then release back to the original pitch.

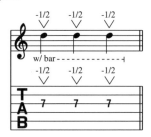

Additional Musical Definitions

 (accent) • Accentuate note (play it louder)

 (accent) • Accentuate note with great intensity

 (staccato) • Play the note short

 • Downstroke

 • Upstroke

D.S. al Coda • Go back to the sign (𝄋), then play until the measure marked "***To Coda***," then skip to the section labelled "**Coda**."

D.C. al Fine • Go back to the beginning of the song and play until the measure marked "***Fine***" (end).

Rhy. Fig. • Label used to recall a recurring accompaniment pattern (usually chordal).

Riff • Label used to recall composed, melodic lines (usually single notes) which recur.

Fill • Label used to identify a brief melodic figure which is to be inserted into the arrangement.

Rhy. Fill • A chordal version of a Fill.

tacet • Instrument is silent (drops out).

 • Repeat measures between signs.

 • When a repeated section has different endings, play the first ending only the first time and the second ending only the second time.

NOTE: Tablature numbers in parentheses mean:
1. The note is being sustained over a system (note in standard notation is tied), or
2. The note is sustained, but a new articulation (such as a hammer-on, pull-off, slide or vibrato begins), or
3. The note is a barely audible "ghost" note (note in standard notation is also in parentheses).